A Pearson Custom Publication

KT-161-301

Get Ready for A&P

Compiled from:

Get Ready for A&P
by Lori K. Garrett

PEARSON
Custom
Publishing

Pearson Education Limited
Edinburgh Gate
Harlow
Essex CM20 2JE

And associated companies throughout the world

Visit us on the World Wide Web at:
www.pearsoned.co.uk

First published 2007

This Custom Book Edition © 2007 Published by Pearson Education Limited

Taken from:

Get Ready for A&P
by Lori K. Garrett
ISBN 0 8053 8284 4
Copyright © 2007 by Pearson Education, Inc., publishing as Pearson Benjamin
Cummings, San Francisco, CA 94111

All rights reserved. No part of this publication may be reproduced, stored in a retrieval
system, or transmitted in any form or by any means, electronic,
mechanical, photocopying, recording or otherwise, without either the prior
written permission of the publisher or a licence permitting restricted copying in the
United Kingdom issued by the Copyright Licensing Agency Ltd, 90
Tottenham Court Road, London W1T 4LP.

ISBN-10 1 84658 344 6
ISBN-13 978 1 84658 344 5

Printed and bound by CPI Antony Rowe, Eastbourne

Contents

Welcome to the fascinating world of anatomy and physiology! Most students take A&P because they have to—it's a required part of their educational curriculum. But I hope you quickly discover how amazing the human body is and become intent on learning all that you possibly can about it. After all, you *are* one!

For many reasons, students sometimes do not succeed in their first anatomy and physiology class. If you're reading this Preface, you probably have a strong desire to succeed, and you know the competition for admission into numerous educational programs is increasing. You are likely keenly aware that you can't just pass your classes—you need to do quality work and truly master the course content. This book offers you the opportunity to enhance your performance in this rigorous course. It is designed to help you gear up to be successful.

You may be using this book before your course officially begins. Your instructor may have assigned it to you as homework during the first week or two of class. Perhaps you are using it on your own and will come back to it periodically throughout the semester as you move along in your course. However you use it, the purpose of the book remains the same. The goal is to help you get a strong start in anatomy and physiology, and to master the material not just for exams, but for your future as well. *Get Ready for A&P* contains six relatively short and interactive chapters that engage you every step of the way. You'll read, but you'll also frequently do activities.

The book starts with basic study skills in **Chapter 1**. As with any course, you will get out of A&P what you put into it, and it will take significant time and effort on your part to succeed. This chapter helps you focus and manage your time so you can first find time to study, then use your study time effectively. After exploring different learning styles you can assess which style best fits you, then discover specific study strategies that compliment your preferred style. You'll assess your current habits as a student and learn specific tips and strategies to help you study better. Specific tips will help you write your notes, read textbooks, and take tests.

Chapter 2 covers basic math skills. Anatomy and physiology are sciences, and all science involves at least some math. This chapter takes you from basic math operations through reading and interpreting numerical information in graphs and tables—the math you'll need for a head start in your course.

Many of the words in your A&P class will sound foreign to you, and well they should! Most of the terms come from Latin or Greek. Knowing the terms underlies all aspects of learning in this class. In **Chapter 3**, Terminology, we look at how the words are built and learn some simple tricks that will rapidly expand your A&P vocabulary and have you talking like a pro!

The second half of the book gets more specific and parallels some of what you will cover in the first few chapters of your A&P textbook. In **Chapter 4**, we cover body basics: some general biological principles that guide how the body works, and a quick overview of each organ system. You'll begin to understand how your body is arranged and how the different systems function.

In **Chapter 5**, we tackle some basic chemistry. This chapter gives you the basics, from atoms to organic molecules. We discuss some neat tricks for gaining information from the Periodic Table, and see how atoms join together to form molecules. If you can understand bumper cars, you can understand bonding!

Finally, in **Chapter 6**, we explore cells. We are made of trillions of them, and almost everything that happens in our bodies occurs inside our cells. We discuss basic cell structure, the cell life cycle, and cell reproduction.

Now that you know the roadmap for this book, let's explore the stops you'll find along the way. Here are the special features in each chapter, designed to keep you involved and to make you a better student in A&P:

- *Your Starting Point* tests your grasp of the chapter content before you start. Answers are provided for all of these except in Chapter 1, where the answers are personal.

- *Quick Check* asks you to recall or apply what you just read, to keep your eyes from scanning the page while your brain is on vacation. The answer is provided on the same page.

- *Picture This* asks you to visualize scenarios and then answer questions about them, to help you better understand the topics.

- *Time to Try* is a simple experiment or quick assessment in which you perform an active exercise.

- *Why Should I Care?* highlights the relevance of the material so you understand its importance in the big picture.

- *Reality Check* assesses whether you really "got" the material.

- *Keys* highlight main themes or statements for reinforcement and easy review.

- *Running Words* lists key terms from the chapter to help you start your own running vocabulary list by writing each term in a notebook, then defining it.

- *What Did You Learn?* end-of-chapter quizzes may include short answer, multiple choice, or matching exercises. The answers appear at the end of the book.

- *Web Resources* provides links to useful Internet sites at which you can learn more or practice what you've learned. Many of these provide additional activities or quizzes as well.

Finally, check out the online component of *Get Ready for A & P* at **www.myaandp.com** or **www.anatomyandphysiology.com**, where you can study and quiz yourself with interactive tutorials, quizzes, animations, flashcards, and an audio glossary.

I wrote *Get Ready for A&P* in a conversational tone because that is how I teach and because science is too often turned boring by boring presentation. Science shouldn't be stuffy—it should be fun! Learning should be peppered with giggles, salted with silliness, and dotted with *AhHA!* moments. Sometimes it seems the terminology alone can put you in a trance, so why should the style?

Now it is time to dig in. So get comfortable, and *Get Ready for A&P!*

Acknowledgments

Ah, where to begin? This project began with what seemed a harmless email from Assistant Editor Jessica Brunner, asking if I would consider submitting a sample chapter for a new workbook. I took the bait. It has been a whirlwind of frenzied activity from that moment, and never have I worked on a project for which the team was more important. To make this book possible, an amazing group pulled together, taking on lots of "other duties as assigned," and ignoring conventional wisdom. I thank Wendy Earl for coming up with a new "Production Paradigm" to make this book happen on an incredibly accelerated schedule, for her rapid turnarounds on copyediting, and for developing a schedule we, surprisingly, found we could almost live with! I thank Randall Goodall for designing the text and keeping it user-friendly, and for so kindly making all our picky revisions. I thank all the gang with him at Seventeenth Street Studios, especially Richard and Valerie, for their work on the paging and art. I thank Kevin "Kartoon" Opstedal for his wonderful cartoon illustrations that kept this book fun, the way science *should* be. And I thank Travis Amos for so quickly getting us just the right photos.

I especially thank the editorial team at Benjamin Cummings. Jessica, thanks for making that initial contact, for all the shipments you sent to me, for being the one left behind when others were traveling, and for all the assorted details you tended to both in and out of my direct line of fire. I wholeheartedly thank Claire Alexander. Claire—I chuckle as I think of you now! I will miss our daily laughs, the lengthy phone chats, and the silliness that kept us both going. And I will always be grateful for the coffee beans—a guaranteed way to help meet tight deadlines. And with greatest respect, I thank Serina Beauparlant for remembering me from previous work and giving me this super opportunity. Serina, you have always made me feel invaluable and been remarkably accommodating. I truly appreciate how closely you followed this project, staying in touch from the road, checking in regularly just to be sure I was happy, and giving me such freedom. I especially thank you for recognizing the need for this project, valuing my skills and knowledge, and pulling together this fantastic and fun team that worked against all odds and that ever-ticking clock to do the impossible. Thanks for my best publishing experience ever.

I also want to extend special thanks to Judy Megaw of Indian River Community College, who took charge of the online component, ensuring a robust website that fully supports this book.

I would be remiss if I didn't thank the many reviewers, listed on the following page, who carefully considered these chapters and gave me their candid feedback—the book is stronger because of their input.

Finally, I gladly acknowledge the home team here at Danville Area Community College. I thank my students for being so supportive and for doing their jobs well so I look good in mine. I thank Donna Davis for getting all those last-minute overnight shipments out the door. I thank Dean Janet Redenbaugh for her constant support of me and all my undertakings, and I thank John Hoagland for putting up with all the insanity and chaos.

—Lori Garrett

REVIEWERS

Erin Amerman
Santa Fe Community College

Vince Austin
Bluegrass Community & Technical College

Claudie Biggers
Amarillo College

Margaret Creech
Laramie County Community College

Terry Harrison
Arapahoe Community College

Clare Hays
Metropolitan State University

Maurice Heller
El Paso Community College

Mark Hubley
Prince George Community College

Catherine Hurlbut
Florida Community College, Jacksonville

Jody Johnson
Arapahoe Community College

Johanna Kruckeberg
Kirkwood Community College

Ken Malachowsky
Florence-Darlington Technical College

Elaine Marieb
Holyoke Community College

Judy Megaw
Indian River Community College

Claire Miller
Community College of Denver

Amy Nunnally
Front Range Community College

Wayne Seifert
Brookhaven College

Alan Spindler
Brevard Community College

Dieterich Steinmetz
Portland Community College

Yong Tang
Front Range Community College

Deborah Temperly
Delta College

Jennifer van de Kamp
Front Range Community College

1 Study Skills

The Proper Care and Feeding of a Human Brain

When you complete this chapter, you should be able to:

■ Understand your preferred learning style and study strategies that emphasize it.

■ Have skills that will help you get the most benefit from lectures and readings.

■ Have a written schedule that includes adequate study time.

■ Know how to prepare well for an exam.

■ Understand that you are ultimately accountable for your own success or failure.

Your Starting Point

Answer the following questions to assess your study habits.

1. How often do you read a course textbook? _____

2. How many days of the week do you study for one course? _____

3. Do you study hard the day before an exam, but rarely between exams?

   _____

4. Where do you study? _____

5. How long should you spend studying outside of class? _____

6. Do you schedule your study time and stick to it? _____

7. Do you study hard or hardly study? _____

8. Do you mostly memorize when studying for a test? _____

9. Do you have a good support group of family and friends who encourage you? _____

10. Do you quiz yourself when studying? _____

Welcome to the exciting and sometimes challenging world of anatomy and physiology! You will quickly discover how amazing the human machine truly is—a curious marvel of complexity that is simultaneously surprisingly simple. I hope you will be fascinated by learning how your own body is built (anatomy) and how it works (physiology). Interest in your subject matter always makes it much easier to learn.

Still, no matter how exciting your anatomical explorations may be, your course may, at times, seem rigorous and demanding. You've taken a great first step by turning to this book to jump-start your studies. This book is meant to help you enter the course with a well-planned strategy

Answers: Answers will be individualized, except for #5—you should spend 2–3 hours studying for each hour of class time.

for success and with confidence in your basic science knowledge. The purpose of this chapter is to help you "train your brain" to make your learning process easier and more efficient.

Why Should I Study Anatomy and Physiology?

Most students take anatomy and physiology because it is required for their educational programs. Sometimes when something is required, we do it only because we have to without considering what benefits the task might hold for us. Unfortunately, some students use that approach for anatomy and physiology. Certainly it is easier to study something if you understand why it matters, and this course is no exception.

PICTURE THIS

Until recently your car has run perfectly, but now the engine occasionally quits running and is difficult to restart. Assuming you have little knowledge of auto mechanics, you are not likely to solve the mystery or make repairs yourself. You take it to an auto mechanic, who will consider how your car is malfunctioning—its symptoms, if you will—and then fix it. What knowledge will the mechanic need to accomplish that goal? _____

_____

_____

In what ways are people in health- and medical-related fields similar to the auto mechanic? _____

_____

Why do they need to fully understand anatomy and physiology?

_____

_____

Now consider your own future—what is your planned career?

_____

Why will you need to know anatomy and physiology?

_____

_____

Many anatomy and physiology students plan careers in a medical or health field. Others may be heading into kinesiology, athletic or personal training, perhaps biomechanics or bioengineering, and many other fields. These career areas share a common thread—anatomy and physiology form the foundation on which they are all built. Now, back to our example. To understand your malfunctioning car, the mechanic must first fully understand the parts of your car—how they fit together and how they normally function, just as you will need to understand the parts of the human body and their normal functions. Finally, there is a simpler reason why you should care about learning anatomy and physiology. The human body is an amazing machine, and you own one. Anatomy and physiology are your owner's manual.

To Thine Own Self Be True: **Learning Styles**

What *is* the best way to learn these subjects? A tremendous amount of research has explored how people learn, and there are many opinions. One common approach considers which of the senses a learner relies on the most—sight, sound, or touch:

- Visual learners learn best by *seeing*.

- Auditory learners learn best by *hearing*.

- Tactile (kinesthetic) learners learn best by *doing*.

TIME TO TRY

Let's uncover your learning style.

1. Look at **Table 1.1**. Read an activity in the first column, then read each of the three responses to the right of that activity.

2. Mark the response that seems most characteristic of you.

3. After doing this for each row, you are ready for your totals. Simply add all the marks in each column and write the total in the corresponding space in the bottom row.

4. Next look at your numbers. You will likely have a higher total in one column. That is your primary learning style. The second high number is your secondary learning style.

My primary learning style is: _____

My secondary learning style: _____

TABLE 1.1   Assessing your learning style.

Activity	Column 1	Column 2	Column 3
1. While I try to **concentrate** . . .	I grow distracted by clutter or movement, and I notice things in my visual field that other people don't.	I get distracted by sounds, and I prefer to control the amount and type of noise around me.	I become distracted by commotion, and I tend to retreat inside myself.
2. While I am **visualizing** . . .	I see vivid, detailed pictures in my thoughts.	I think in voices and sounds.	I see images in my thoughts that involve movement.
3. When I **talk to someone** . . .	I dislike listening for very long.	I enjoy listening, or I may get impatient to talk.	I gesture and use expressive movements.
4. When I **contact people** . . .	I prefer face-to-face meetings.	I prefer speaking by telephone for intense conversations.	I prefer to interact while walking or participating in some activity.

▶

TABLE 1.1 Assessing your learning style, continued.

Activity	Column 1	Column 2	Column 3
5. When I **see an acquaintance** . . .	I tend to forget names but usually remember faces, and I can usually remember where we met.	I tend to remember people's names and can usually remember what we discussed.	I tend to remember what we did together and may almost "feel" our time together.
6. When I am **relaxing** . . .	I prefer to watch TV, see a play, or go to a movie.	I prefer to listen to the radio, play music, read, or talk with a friend.	I prefer to play sports, make crafts, or build something with my hands.
7. While I am **reading** . . .	I like descriptive scenes and may pause to imagine the action.	I enjoy the dialogue most and can "hear" the characters talking.	I prefer action stories, but I rarely read for pleasure.
8. When I am **spelling** . . .	I try to see the word in my mind or imagine what it would look like on paper.	I sound out the word, sometimes aloud, and tend to recall rules about letter order.	I get a feel for the word by writing it out or pretending to type it.
9. When I **do something new** . . .	I seek out demonstrations, pictures or diagrams.	I like verbal and written instructions, and talking it over with someone else.	I prefer to jump right in to try it, and I will keep trying and try different ways.

TABLE 1.1 Assessing your learning style, continued.

Activity	Column 1	Column 2	Column 3
10. When I **assemble something** . . .	I look at the picture first and then, maybe, read the directions.	I like to read the directions, or I talk aloud as I work.	I usually ignore the directions and figure it out as I go along.
11. When I am **interpreting someone's mood** . . .	I mostly look at his or her facial expressions.	I listen to the tone of the voice.	I watch body language.
12. When I **teach others how to do something** . . .	I prefer to show them how to do it.	I prefer to tell them or write out how to do it.	I demonstrate how it is done and ask them to try.
TOTAL:	**Visual:** _____	**Auditory:** _____	**Tactile/Kinesthetic:** _____

[Source: Courtesy of Marcia L. Conner, www.agelesslearner.com]

Now that you know your primary and secondary learning styles, you can design your study approach accordingly, emphasizing activities that use your preferred senses. Look closely at your scores, though. If two scores are rather close, you already use two learning styles well and will benefit from using both of them when studying. If your high score is much higher than your other scores, you have a strong preference and should particularly emphasize that style. Most people use a combination of learning styles.

In addition, information coming in through different senses reaches different parts of your brain. The more of your brain that is engaged in the learning process, the more effective your learning will be, so try strategies for all three styles and merely emphasize your preferred style over the others. You'll know which strategies work best for you. We'll consider some strategies that you might try for each style; these ideas are summarized for you in Table 1.2.

TABLE 1.2   The three learning styles and helpful techniques to use in your studies.

	Visual	Auditory	Tactile
Techniques to use	❏ Sit close to the teacher. ❏ Take detailed notes. ❏ Draw pictures. ❏ Make flow charts. ❏ Use flash cards. ❏ Focus on the figures, tables, and their captions. ❏ Try coloring books and picture atlases. ❏ Use visualization.	❏ Listen carefully to your teacher's voice. ❏ Read the textbook and your notes out loud. ❏ Tape record lectures and listen to them later. ❏ Listen during class instead of writing notes. ❏ Work in a study group. ❏ Discuss the material with others.	❏ Highlight important information while reading. ❏ Write your own notes in class and while reading the textbook. ❏ Transfer your notes to another tablet or type into your computer. ❏ Doodle and draw as you read. ❏ Build models of anatomical structures. ❏ Create and conduct your own experiments. ❏ Hold your book while reading. ❏ Walk or stand while reading. ❏ Use anatomy coloring books. ❏ Use flash cards.

VISUAL LEARNERS

If you are a **visual learner**, you rely heavily on visual cues. You notice your teacher's mannerisms, expressions, gestures, and body language. Seeing these cues is especially helpful, so sit at the front of the classroom, close to the teacher. You tend to think in pictures and learn well from visual aids such as diagrams, illustrations, tables, videos, and hand-outs. Here are some strategies for you.

- In class, take detailed notes and make sketches.

- When studying on your own, draw pictures that relate to the information, make flow charts and concept maps, use flash cards, focus on illustrations and tables in your textbook, and read the captions that accompany them.

- Use anatomy and physiology coloring books and picture atlases.

- Use mental visualization of the material you are studying and imagine yourself acting out processes. For example, to learn major blood vessels, you might imagine yourself swimming through them.

AUDITORY LEARNERS

If you are an **auditory learner**, you learn well from traditional lectures and discussion. You listen carefully to your teacher's vocal pitch, tone, speed, and mannerisms. Material that you struggle with while reading becomes clearer when you hear it. Here are some strategies for you.

- Read the textbook and your notes out loud.

- Tape record the lectures so you can listen to them later. Taping lectures also allows you to listen during class instead of focusing on writing, which is less beneficial for you.

- Work in a study group, and discuss material with your teacher, lab group, and friends.

TACTILE LEARNERS

If you are a **tactile learner**, you learn best by actively participating and doing hands-on activities. You may become bored easily in class from sitting still too long and start fidgeting or doodling. You need to do something physical while studying and learning. Here are some strategies for you.

- Try using a marker to highlight important information while you are reading.

- Write out your own notes in class and while reading the textbook. Later, transfer your notes to another tablet or type them into your computer.

- Draw pictures of appropriate material as you read.

- Build models of anatomical structures using clay or other materials.

- Create and conduct your own experiments.

- Hold your book and walk while reading.

- Use anatomy coloring books.

- Make and use your own flash cards.

- Keep your hands and your mind busy together.

WHY SHOULD I CARE?

Understanding your own learning style allows you to develop more effective and efficient study techniques that take advantage of your sensory preferences. By emphasizing your preferred learning style, the material will be easier to learn and will stay with you longer.

✔ **QUICK CHECK**

Homemade flash cards would be most beneficial to which two learning styles? _____ and _____.
How could they be used to benefit a learner of the third style?

_____

Answer: They would benefit visual and tactile learners. Reading them out loud would benefit auditory learners.

Putting on Your Best Face: **Getting Ready**

Many students mistakenly wait until the first lecture to start thinking about class. The key to starting your semester well is to be organized and ready when you enter the classroom. This takes advance planning, but the time invested will save you tremendous time while the semester is underway.

PUTTING IT IN WRITING

As the semester begins—if not before—you should get organized, and that begins with making a commitment to yourself. Too often we begin a project without setting goals in advance. If you set a goal, you enter with a purpose and a direction. If you do not set a goal, it's too easy to just go along and see where you end. Take time to think about your goals for the semester. They should be both specific and attainable. Be realistic. For example, it may not be realistic to set the goal of always having the highest score in class, but a goal of getting an A in the class might be attainable. Once you've decided on your goals, write them down to give them more importance. Once you've written them, be firmly committed to them. To reinforce these goals, write them on an index card and place it in a prominent location in your study area so you'll see them every day.

TIME TO TRY

Set three main goals for yourself in this class, and write them below. Explain why achieving each goal is important to you.

Goal 1: _____

*It is important to me because:*_____

_____

Goal 2: _____

*It is important to me because:*_____

_____

Goal 3: _____

*It is important to me because:*_____

_____

PULLING IT ALL TOGETHER

I'm amazed when students show up for a test with no writing utensils! Don't let that happen to you. The more organized you are, the more efficient you will be, so let's organize what you will need for class. Categorize the items by what you take to class every day, what remains at home in your study spot, and optional items that are nice, but nonessential, additions. Use the checklist provided for you in **Table 1.3.** Search your house and you'll likely find that you have many of these items already. Most items can be bought at your college bookstore, but many are available at discount stores. We will discuss some of these items specifically.

You'll be going back and forth to class a lot, so it is most efficient to keep all the items you might need for class in one place. To haul them, most students use a book bag, backpack, or briefcase. An advantage to using one of these is that you can load it up with the essentials so that they are always ready to walk out the door with you. Let's discuss some of the items to pack.

You need a pocket-sized day planner that has plenty of room for writing and that you can keep with you at all times. Or you may opt for a personal organizer portfolio or an electronic organizer. Select one you like, because you'll use it every day. In it, write all important dates you already

TABLE 1.3	Organizer's checklist.	
Item		✎✗
To take to class each day:		
Book bag/backpack/rolling carrier		
Textbooks/lab manuals		
Pocket-sized day planner		
To Do List		
Separate notebooks for each course		
Copy of class schedule with buildings and room numbers		
Several blue or black ink pens		
Several #2 pencils		
Small pencil sharpener		
2–3 colored highlighter pens		
Small stapler		
Grade record sheet for each course		
Calculator		
At home:		
Master calendar		
Separate file or folder for each course		
Loose notebook paper		
Index cards for making flash cards		
Computer paper (if I have a computer)		
More writing utensils (pens and pencils)		
Stapler		
Calculator		
Scissors		
Paper clips		
Optional:		
Personal organizer		
Anatomy coloring book		
Colored markers/pencils		
Small tape recorder to record lectures/readings		
Recording tapes		
Extra batteries		
Anatomy atlas		
Medical dictionary		

know—when classes begin, holidays, last day to withdraw from a class, when finals begin. Enter all class times, your work schedule, and any other known time commitments. Try to keep your day planner current so you always know how your time is being spent and can plan ahead.

If it's not part of your day planner, you need a separate To Do List. You will write all assignments and due dates on this list. You want one single To Do List for all of your classes as well as non-school activities, because they must all be done from the same pool of time. Writing them down allows you to view the entire list and review the deadlines for each item so you can easily prioritize, doing the assignments in the order in which they are due.

Maintain a record of all grades you receive (**Figure 1.1**). For each graded item, list what it is, when you turned it in, when you got it back, how many points you received, how many points were possible, and any additional notes. Once you know how your grade will be determined for the course, you can use this to keep track as you go along. It also provides a backup in case there is any confusion later about your grade or your work.

Graded item	Date turned in	Date returned	My score	Possible points	Notes
Lab 1	9/6	9/13	10	10	Worked with Emily, Mike, Tom
Quiz 1	9/7	9/9	18	20	Study terms again
Lab 2	9/13	9/16	6	10	Messed up the math!
Pop Quiz	9/14	9/16	5	5	From yesterday's lecture. I was ready!
Quiz 2	9/21	9/25	19	20	Forgot to answer one question!

FIGURE 1.1   A sample grade record for keeping track of your progress.

Check with your instructor to see if you should bring your textbook to class. Typically, you may not need it in lecture.

And for lecture, always carry the basics. You need a note-book for note-taking. If you come to my class without a writing utensil, it says you do not think that what I am saying is important enough for notes. If you ask me for a stapler before turning in an assignment, it says you threw it together with little thought. Pens, pencils, erasers, staples, paper, highlighters, colored pencils, index cards, paper clips—these are just some items you may find useful. Replenish your supply as needed.

Set up your home study space like a home office. Be sure to have all the essential office supplies on hand—plenty of writing utensils, paper, a stapler, and so on. A critical part of the home study area is the master calendar. There are large desktop versions and wall charts, for example. You could use a calendar feature on your computer, but the more visible the calendar is, the more often you will look at it. This calendar should be large enough to accommodate plenty of writing, so think BIG! Each day, you should add anything that you put in your day planner or on your To Do List to this master calendar. All time commitments should be entered, so also add all personal appointments and vacations. This is how you will schedule your life while in school, and the practice will likely stick with you far beyond that.

You may have already started your class before using this workbook. You certainly cannot do all these things before class at this point, but it is never too late to get organized. So, go get it together!

✔ **QUICK CHECK**

To be successful in class, your effort should start before class begins. What are some tasks you should do before the first day of class?

_____

_____

_____

Set and write down your goals, organize the items you will need for class and at home, pack your carrier, start your day planner and master calendar, and organize your study space.

I Hate to **Lecture** on this, but Can You Hear Me Now?

Welcome to class! Imagine that it is the first day. You walk into class.

Where do you sit? _____

Why do you sit there? _____

The best seat in the house is front and center. Obviously not everyone can sit there, but you should arrive early enough to sit within the first few rows and as near to the middle as possible. You want an unobstructed view of the instructor and anything he or she might show, because anatomy is often a very visual course. People sitting on the sides or in the back often do not want to be called on, or they want to be in their own space. They are not very engaged in the class. Don't let that be you. To succeed, you need to focus all of your attention on your instructor, minimize distractions, and actively participate. Instructors tend to teach to the middle of the room (**Figure 1.2**). In fact, if your instructor is right-handed and uses equipment, such as an overhead projector, that is positioned on the right, the instructor's focus shifts to his or her right. You want to see your instructor and you want your instructor to see that you are present, actively listening, and engaged.

Some instructors provide lecture notes so you can sit back and really think about what is being said. Notes or not, you need to get all the information you can from each lecture. Remember your learning style and use techniques that enhance it. We will discuss note-taking momentarily, but consider tape recording the lectures. That way you miss nothing, and you can listen to the tape repeatedly, rewinding as needed. Another good technique is to write out your own notes while listening to the tape, then listen again while reading your notes and making necessary corrections. This combination strongly reinforces the material.

Always try to preview the material that will be covered before going to class. This is as simple as lightly reading the corresponding sections in the textbook. You may not understand all that you read, but it will sound familiar and be easier to comprehend as your instructor covers it in class. This preview also helps you identify new vocabulary words.

While your instructor is lecturing, don't hesitate to raise your hand to ask a question or get clarification. Many students are shy and reluctant to speak in class—you may be doing them a favor! Avoid discussing

FIGURE 1.2 Main areas of focus for an instructor. The larger shaded area shows where the instructor looks most often. The smaller shaded area shows how that focal area shifts to the right as the instructor uses equipment positioned to the right.

personal issues in front of the whole class—that is better done alone with the instructor, outside the classroom.

Note your instructor's gestures, facial expressions, and voice tone for clues about what your instructor finds most important. That material is likely to show up on a quiz or test. Write down any material that is particularly emphasized, or mark it in your notes. Listen carefully for assignments and write them down immediately on your To Do List. If you are not clear about the expectations of the assignment or when it is due, seek immediate clarification.

 QUICK CHECK

Why is it best to sit front and center in class?

_____

_____

Answer: You will be more engaged in the class, have the best view and fewer distractions, and be within your instructor's focal area.

Passing **Notes**

Anybody can take notes in class, but will the notes be good enough to help them succeed in the class? There are many strategies and models for how to take notes, and none of them is necessarily the best. Find what works for you, then use it consistently. Let's review one easy-to-use system (**Figure 1.3**).

Start with a full-sized (A4) notebook that you will use just for this class. Take your notes on only the front side of the paper and leave about a 2" margin on the left. The margin will be used for marking key words and concepts later. At the beginning of class, date the top of the page so you know when the material was covered. During lecture, use an outline format to get as much information down as you can. Use the main concept as a major heading, then indent the information discussed on that topic. When that section ends, either draw a horizontal line to mark its end or leave a couple of blank lines. Don't try to write every word—just the main ideas—and put them in your own words. Instead of writing out every example, give a brief summary or a one- or

RECALL:	03/14/06
Note-taking	I. Note taking tips
	A. Use outline format
	B. Be concise
	C. Get main ideas
Reviewing	II. Reviewing notes
	A. Review after class
	1. Fill in gaps
	2. Clean up
	3. Replay lecture in my mind
	4. Review within 24 hours—fresh in mind.
3 learning styles	III. Learning styles
	A. Visual—reread and add drawings
	B. Tactile—rewrite or type
	C. Auditory—read out loud or tape record

FIGURE 1.3   Sample of lecture notes using the outline style and leaving room in the left margin.

two-word reminder. Use abbreviations when possible, and develop your own shorthand. You can often drop most of the vowels in a word and still be able to sound it out later when reading it. Write legibly or your efforts will be useless later. Underline new or stressed terms and place a star or an arrow by anything that is emphasized. Be as thorough as you can, but you will need to write very quickly. The instructor will not wait for you to catch up, so speed is essential.

As soon as possible after class, read your notes and improve them as necessary. Add anything that's missing. Make them clearer and cleaner. Put the concepts in your own words. Next, use the left margin to summarize each section—the main concept, subtopics, and key terms. The latter column will be your "Recall" column. Once you are sure all of the key ideas are in the left column, you can cover the right side of the page—the meat of your notes—and quiz yourself on the main points listed in the left column. It makes an easy way to review.

But you are not finished—if you are a tactile learner, rewrite your notes in another notebook or type them into your computer. Visual learners might type and reorganize the notes. Auditory learners can read the notes out loud or record them. You can make flash cards from the key points and terms by writing the term on one side of an index card and its definition or use on the other side. You can add drawings. Review your notes as much as you can during the next 24 hours while the lecture is still fresh in your mind.

TIME TO TRY

Look at the sample notes in Figure 1.3. Now practice: Take notes using this style while listening to a 1-hour TV show. Capture the conversations and action in words. You can't get every word down, so paraphrase—put it in your own words so the meaning still comes across. When you're finished, assess how you did.

Can you tell who was talking? _____

Do your notes make sense? _____

Did you capture the main ideas? _____

Did you keep up or fall behind? _____

Do you have breaks in your notes to separate the main conversations and action? _____

What can you do better while taking notes in class?

_____

✔ **QUICK CHECK**

What should you do with your notes after class? _____

_____

_____

Answer: Review them within 24 hours, fill in anything missing, clean them up, put them into your own words, add key concepts and terms to the Recall column, add drawings, make flash cards, record them, rewrite or type them.

Looking for Some-body Special

Your anatomy and physiology class comes in two parts: lecture and practicals. Many students put most of their effort into the lecture material and disregard the lab component. Avoid this. Practical class is the hands-on part of the course, and most people learn better by seeing demonstrations and actually doing the work themselves. Also, part of your grade comes from your performance in practicals. Always go to the skills lab prepared to take notes, equipped with your lab manual, if required, and your textbook if it will be needed.

When in practicals, you may work with a partner or group. You will be expected to contribute equally to the team effort, so it is important that you arrive prepared. If you know in advance what the practical will be, read through it and think about what you will be doing. Pay attention to the instructions and especially note any safety precautions. At times you will be working with very expensive equipment and specimens, and perhaps potentially dangerous materials, so always use great care.

Some students try to take shortcuts so they can leave a bit early. You should value the time to further explore the material covered in lectures. You get to hold the bones, microscopically examine various tissues, use models and charts, and perhaps see real organs or cadavers. It is a unique aspect of your education that reinforces everything else that you are learning. You will spend much time learning structures, and the more you go over them, the better you will recall them. The more time you spend, the more you learn. Remember that lecture and practicals are both part of the same class, and try to see how they fit together. Never leave early—there's always more to learn.

QUICK CHECK

What are some of the learning advantages gained from attending practical sessions? _____

_____

Answer: Time for exploration, hands-on learning, collaboration, and discussion.

 The more time you spend in lab, the better you will learn. ▪

Your Secret Life **Outside of Class**

REALITY CHECK

Answer True or False to each of the following statements:

1. I study the day before a test but rarely study on a daily basis.

   T   F

2. I mostly review my notes and don't read the textbook.

   T   F

3. I am too busy to study each day.

   T   F

4. When I finally get around to it, I study pretty hard for a long time.

   T   F

5. I get by fine with cramming.

   T   F

JUST FOR FUN

Let's see how good a studier you REALLY are! Take a few moments to learn these terms. We will come back to this exercise a bit later.

1. **Frizzled greep.** This is a member of the *Teroplicanis domesticus* family with girdish jugwumps and white frizzles.

2. **Gleendoggled frinlap.** This is a relatively large fernmeiker blib found only in sproingy sugnipers.

3. **Borky-globed dungwinger.** This groobler has gallerific phroonts and is the size of a pygmy wernocked frit.

Stay tuned!

You made it through, and are ready to head home. Finally!

Uni is done for the day, right? Not if you plan to be successful! The real work begins after class, because most of your learning occurs outside the classroom on your own. This is often the hardest part, for many reasons. We schedule many activities and set aside time for them, but studying tends to get crammed into the cracks. Too often, studying becomes what you do when you "get around to it." It is an obligation that often gets crowded out by other daily activities, and the first item dropped from the To Do List.

Too many students only study when they have to—before a quiz or exam. A successful student studies every day. The goal is to learn the material as you go rather than frantically try to memorize a large amount at the last minute. Here is something you need to know and really take to heart.

You should study for at least two to three hours for every hour spent in class. ▧

Simple maths shows you that if you have three lectures on Monday, for example, you should plan to spend from six to nine hours studying that same day. YIKES!

SCHEDULE YOUR STUDY TIME

Writing assignments on your To Do List makes them seem more urgent, but that does not cover the daily work that must be done. You must take charge of your time and studying. In addition to specific assignments, each day you should:

- go over that day's notes,

- read the corresponding sections in the textbook,

- quiz yourself,

- review your notes again, and

- preview the next day's material.

All of this takes time. You must build study time into your schedule or you either will not get around to it or you will put it off until you are too tired to study effectively. The first thing to do is to write your study time into your day planner and master calendar, and regard that time as sacred—do not borrow from it to do something else. Be sure to allow break time during study sessions as well—if you study for too long, your brain gets weary and starts to wander, and it takes much longer to do even simple tasks. Plan a 10- to 15-minute break for every hour of studying.

CHUNK IT

If a job seems too large, we put it off, but if we have many small tasks, each alone seems manageable. Break your workload into small chunks. Write them down, partly so you do not forget any, but especially because you will get a great feeling of accomplishment when you complete a task and cross it off your To Do List! Completing a task is also a convenient time to take a mini-break to keep your mind fresh. Many students try to read a whole chapter or cover a few weeks of notes in one sitting. The brain really dislikes that. When studying a large amount of material, divide it into subcategories, then study one until you really understand it before moving to the next.

STUDY ACTIVELY

Merely reading your notes or the book is not learning. You must think about the material and become an **active learner**. Constantly ask yourself, "What is most important in this section?" While reading, take notes or underline key terms and major concepts. Make flash cards. Consider how what you are studying relates to something with which you are already familiar. If you can put the information in a familiar context, you will retain it better.

The best preparation for quizzes and tests is practice. Develop and answer questions as you read. Try to anticipate all the ways your instructor might quiz you about that material. Recall which specific items your instructor stressed. Outline the material in each section and be sure to understand how the different concepts are related. Check yourself on the meanings of the key terms. Say the key words out loud and look carefully at them. Do they remind you of anything? Have you heard them before?

MOVE PAST MEMORIZING

This is one of the hardest study traps to avoid. In anatomy and physiology, it may at times seem like there is so much to learn and so little time. Most students at first attempt to just memorize. If you only read your notes and the book, you are using this approach without realizing it.

At the beginning of this section, I gave you three items to learn. Without turning back, write down the three names I asked you to learn a few pages ago:

1. _____

2. _____

3. _____

Did you remember them? Now, also without looking back, can you explain each of them to me? _____
(I am betting not)

These three "things" are fictitious, but my point is that you may, indeed, have memorized the names—it doesn't take much to memorize—but it takes a lot more to understand, especially if the words are unfamiliar, as they often are in this course. If you find that you study hard but the wording of the quiz or test confuses you, I can almost guarantee that you are memorizing. The question is worded a bit differently than what you memorized, so you don't realize that you know the answer. You must get past memorizing by looking for relationships between the concepts and terms, and really strive for full understanding. Reading often produces memorization. Active studying produces understanding.

THE CONCEPT MAP

A very useful technique for learning relationships is drawing a **concept map.** This is somewhat like brainstorming. Here is the general process:

1. Start with a blank piece of (preferably) unlined paper.

2. Near the center, draw a circle and, inside it, list the main concept you will explore.

3. Around that circle, and allowing some space, draw more circles and list in each anything that pops into your mind related to your main concept. Do this quickly and don't think about the relationships yet. Just get your ideas down.

4. Once you've added all your secondary concepts, look at them and think about how they are related, not just to the main concept but to each other as well.

5. As relationships occur to you, draw arrows connecting related concepts and add a brief description of the relationship between each of the concepts.

6. Examine the relationships and you will start to understand how these concepts fit together.

TIME TO TRY

Construct a concept map around the main concept of *energy* by adding arrows to show relationships between the following concepts:

■ cell activity,

■ food,

- plants,

- the Sun, and

- work.

When you are finished, look at **Figure 1.4**, below.

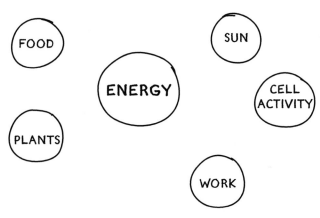

First draw a circle or "node" for each concept, keeping the main concept, if there is one, near the middle.

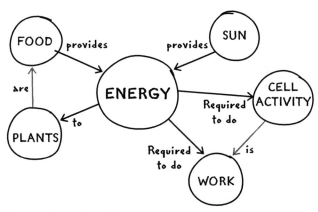

Next, add arrows linking the different concepts to each other, then add brief descriptions of how they are linked. In this example, the arrows show that the sun provides energy to the plants, plants are food that provides energy that is required to do cell activity, which is a type of work.

FIGURE 1.4   Drawing a concept map.

REVIEW

OK, you've been at this study thing for awhile and you think you're starting to get the material. You did all of the above; can you quit now? Almost, but once you think you have the material under control, review it one more time. Repetition is the key to your long-term memory—the more you go over the material, the longer it will stay with you. I always recommend a minimum of three passes, even for easy stuff—read your notes, read the text, re-read your notes—and that assumes you are understanding the material. Always slow down and go through it more if you are struggling with a certain section. Use **active learning** with each pass, then finish with one more review. If you are alert enough to review right before bed, once you are asleep your brain often continues going over the material without bothering you too much (although one of my students reported a dream in which she was chased by a herd of giant bones!).

The website for your textbook also provides a good way to review. The address is in your book. Most book websites offer a wide variety of activity options, perhaps including online animations, flashcards, puzzles, objectives, vocabulary lists, and quizzes. When taking online quizzes, be sure to do so without looking in your book or your notes—after all, you do not use them for quizzes in class. Not using them provides a better simulation of the classroom experience. And, if you do well on the online quizzes without using your notes, you will have confidence in the classroom knowing you have already passed one quiz!

NO CRAMMING ALLOWED!

I have a very busy life, so my house occasionally gets a bit cluttered. If company drops by and it is a "bad house day," I might quickly grab some of the clutter and cram it into a spare closet. After the guests leave, I open the closet door to pull out a quilt. What happens? _____

_____

Now imagine what you do to your brain when you cram for an exam. You are essentially opening the closet door and cramming stuff in, then slamming the door. When you are taking the test, you open the door to pull out the answer you need, but anything might tumble onto your paper. Cramming at best allows partial memorization. At worst, it causes the information to get mixed up and you fail. It is a desperate act of superficial studying guaranteed to NOT get you through anatomy and physiology. If you study on a daily basis instead of doing a panicky cram session before a test, you will be calmly reviewing what you already learned well and smiling at the crammers in class.

NO VAMPIRES ALLOWED!

*Do you think you can pull an all-nighter and really do well?*_____

What do you think are some of the reasons this will not work? _____

_____

If you normally live your life by day, you cannot suddenly override your natural biological clock and expect your brain to stay alert and focused when it knows it is supposed to be asleep. Caffeine may help keep your eyes open, but you'll only be a tad more alert and jittery while still yawning and mentally drifting away from the task at hand. The only reason you would need to stay up all night is if you haven't been studying all along and this is your last option. It is not effective. You will not be mentally alert. You will not be able to focus or think through the material. Your eyes may skim the pages, but you'll struggle to comprehend the words and you'll retain only a tiny amount of the very little that you absorb.

An all-nighter is basically a marathon cram session held at the worst possible time. It simultaneously robs your brain and body of what they need—restoration before the next day. You may be able to stay awake all night, but if you doze off you may oversleep and miss your exam. Or, if you do arrive (I hope you weren't driving with no sleep!), you may get part way into the test only to have your brain bail on you. If you are prone to "test anxiety," your defenses will be down and you will quite likely freeze and fail. Ah, if only you had been studying all along . . .

For your brain to be kind to you, you have to be kind to its home. You must take care of yourself physically—eat, sleep, exercise, and RELAX. ■

✔ **QUICK CHECK**

Why should you study every day if the test is not for two weeks?

_____

_____

Answer: Studying on a regular basis breaks the material into smaller more manageable pieces that you can master; the material is fresh in your mind, and you will only need to review it before the test.

Strength in Numbers: **The Study Group**

One of the best ways to learn anything is to teach it to someone else, so form a study group or discuss the material with others around you (**Figure 1.5**). Although this may not be the best option for everyone, it is highly effective for many students. As soon as possible, start asking your classmates who wants to be in a study group—you *will* get people to join. You can quiz each other, discuss the material, help each other, and quite importantly, support each other. If you study solo, you may not be

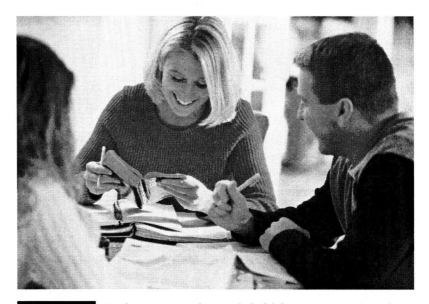

FIGURE 1.5   Study groups can be very helpful for staying motivated and focused on course material.

aware of your weaknesses. Your study partners can help identify them and help you overcome them. A good way to work in a study group is to split up the material and assign different sections to different members, who then master the material and teach it to the group. Each member should also be studying it all on his or her own—that ensures better effort from everyone, and allows other members to correct any errors in a presentation.

Scheduling joint study sessions can be challenging. Many students find that scheduling group sessions before or after class works best. You may want to establish some ground rules, including agreeing to use the time for studying and not for gossiping or just socializing. And although it may be tempting to meet over a pizza, you do want a quiet location where you can freely discuss the material with few distractions. Check with your instructor to see if there are any times that might work for this.

SQRHuh? **How to Read a Textbook**

The name may sound odd, but **SQR3** is an effective method for studying your textbook. Science textbooks do not read like novels, so you need to approach them differently. This method also works well for reviewing your notes. It stands for:

- Survey

- Question

- Read

- Recite

- Review

During the **survey phase,** read the chapter title, the chapter introduction, any other items at the beginning of the chapter, and all of the headings. This gives you the road map of where you will be going in the chapter. As you skim the chapter, also read all items in bold or italic. Next, read the chapter summary at the end of the chapter.

During the **question phase**, look at the heading of each section and form as many questions as you can that you think may be covered in that section. Write them down. Try to be comprehensive in this step. By having these questions in mind, you will automatically search for answers as you read.

Now **read** the chapter for details. Take your time. Adjust your reading speed with the difficulty of the material. Also, keep in mind the questions you developed and try to answer them.

The next phase is to **recite**. You are working on your ability to recall information. After reading each section, think about your questions and try to answer them from recall. If you cannot, reread the section and try again. Continue this cycle until you can recite the answers.

Finally, you want to **review**. This helps reinforce your memory. After you complete the previous steps for the sections you're studying, go back to each heading and see if you can still answer all of your questions. Repeat the recite phase until you can. When you are done, be sure you can also answer the questions at the end of the chapter.

✔ **QUICK CHECK**

What is SQR3 and what do the letters mean?

_____

_____

Answer: It is a system for reading a textbook, and the letters mean Survey, Question, Read, Recite, and Review.

A Place to Call My Own: **The Study Environment**

Briefly describe the location where you plan to do most of your studying.

_____

_____

_____

Now you know how to study effectively, but we often overlook WHERE to study. Your options may be limited, so you need to make the best of what you have. Ideally your study spot is somewhat isolated and free of distractions like TV, music, and people. At the least, you should minimize distractions.

Do you study in front of a TV that is on? Even if you try hard to ignore it, you will be drawn to it, especially if the material you are studying is tough. Music can be tricky—songs that you know, especially lively ones, may get you tapping and singing along with them while you think your mind is actively engaged in learning. However, soft or classical music can keep you calm and more focused, unless you really dislike that kind of music.

Thinking about the study site you listed above, what distractions might you face? _____

_____

How can you minimize them? _____

If you cannot, seek another study spot. _____

For studying, you really need a space that is your own. A desk is a good place (unless it is also the computer desk at which you spend hours playing computer games for fun!). Ideally it will be a place where you do nothing but study, so that when you are seated there you know exactly what your purpose is. If you are having trouble staying on task in your work spot, get up and walk away briefly. The mental and physical break may help you "come back" to work, and you won't begin associating the spot with struggling. Your study spot should be quiet and it should have good lighting to avoid eye strain, a comfortable chair, good ventilation and temperature, and a work surface on which you can spread out.

You will spend a lot of time studying here, so take time initially to set up your study space. The area should be uncluttered and well organized. It should also be inspiring and motivational. Perhaps frame a sign that says *"I WILL be a _____(your career)_____ by __(your goal date)___ ."* Try this same approach for the goals you set at the beginning of this chapter, and display them boldly and prominently. Consider displaying a photo of your hero, or of someone in the family whom you want to make proud. Parents, you might display a photo of your children with a caption saying something like "You are my reason," or "I will teach by example." Realize that you are their role model—your children's attitudes toward education will be formed by what you do now. With these treasures surrounding you, you're a mere glance away from being rein-vigorated if a study session starts to fizzle.

WHY SHOULD I CARE?

Most of your learning is done outside of class. The more efficient your studying, the better you will learn. Your study spot affects your attitude and concentration. The more seriously you take your study location, the more seriously you will study there.

If you live with family or a roommate, you absolutely must stress to them the importance of respecting your study time and study space. Be sure they know your career goals and why they are important to you, and ask them to help by giving you the time and space you need to succeed. Ask them not to disturb you when you are in your space. If you have small children who want time with mommy or daddy while you are studying, assuming they have adequate supervision, try getting them to play or study on their own until "the clock hands are in these positions," then do something fun with them at that time. They will learn to antici-pate your time together and to leave you alone if the reward is worth-while. If you have too many distractions at home, the solution is to study elsewhere. Whether on campus, in the local library, or at a friend's house, you need a distraction-free setting, and if you can't get it at home, remove yourself instead of trying to cope with a poor study space.

✔ QUICK CHECK

What are some of the main considerations in selecting your study spot? _____

_____

Answer: Few distractions, own space just for studying, comfortable, good light-ing/ventilation, sufficient work space, and welcoming.

My, How **Time** Flies!

You know you need to study and that it takes a lot of time, but how will you fit it in? Let's discuss a few ways to budget time for studying. First, be consistent. Consider your schedule to see if you can study at the same time each day. Studying will become a habit more easily if you always do it at the same time. Some students adhere to one schedule on weekdays and a different one on weekends. When scheduling study time, consider your other obligations and how distracted you might be by other people's activities at those times. Don't overlook free hours you might have while on campus. Head to the library, study room, or a quiet corner. This is the ideal time to preview for the next class or to review what was just covered.

TIME TO TRY

This is a two-part exercise designed to help you find your study time.

Part A: Each week has a total of 168 hours. How do you spend *yours*? **Table 1.4** on page 36 allows you to quickly approximate how you spend your time each week.

1. Complete the assessment in Table 1.4 to see how many hours are left each week for you to study.

2. Enter that number here. _____ hours

Part B: Next, turn your attention to **Table1.5** on page 37.

1. Enter your class schedule, work schedule, and any other activities in which you regularly participate.

2. Now look for times when you can schedule study sessions and write them in.

3. Are you able to schedule 2 to 3 hours of study time per hour of class time? _____

It can be difficult, but it is essential to make the time. Writing it into your schedule makes it more likely to happen.

TABLE 1.4 Assessing how your time is spent. For each item in this inventory, really think before answering and be as honest as possible. Items that are done each day must be multiplied by 7 to get your weekly total. One item may be done any number of times a week, so you'll need to multiply that item by the number of times each week you do it. After you have responded to all the questions, you'll have an opportunity to see how many hours remain during the week for studying.

Where Does Your Time Go? Record the number of hours you spend:	How many hours per day?	How many days per week?	Total hours per week: (hours × days)
1. **Grooming,** including showering, shaving, dressing, makeup, and so on.			
2. **Dining,** including preparing food, eating, and cleaning up.			
3. **Commuting** to and from class and work, from door to door.			
4. **Working** at your place of employment.			
5. **Attending class.**			
6. **Doing chores** at home, including housework, mowing, laundry, and so on.			
7. **Caring** for family, a loved one, or a pet.			
8. On **extracurricular activities** such as clubs, church, volunteering.			
9. **Doing errands.**			
10. On **solo recreation,** including TV, reading, games, working out, and so on.			
11. **Socializing,** including parties, phone calls, hanging out, dating, and so on.			
12. **Sleeping** (don't forget those naps!)			
Now add all numbers in the far column to get the total time you spend on all these activities.			
		Hours/week	168
		Total hours spent on other activities −	
		Left for studying =	

Don't overbook! Be sure to build in break time during and between your study sessions, especially the longer ones. Allow for flexibility—realize that unexpected events occur, so be sure you have some extra

TABLE 1.5 My study schedule.

Time	Monday	Tuesday	Wednesday	Thursday	Friday	Saturday
6:00 AM						
7:00 AM						
8:00 AM						
9:00 AM						
10:00 AM						
11:00 AM						
Noon						
1:00 PM						
2:00 PM						
3:00 PM						
4:00 PM						
5:00 PM						
6:00 PM						
7:00 PM						
8:00 PM						
9:00 PM						
10:00 PM						
11:00 PM						
Midnight						

time available. Also, be sure you plan for and schedule recreation, too. You cannot and should not study all the time, but these other activities do take time and need to be in your schedule as well, so that you do not double-book yourself.

Putting It to **The Test**

If I had a pound for every student who said they have test anxiety . . .

Some people really do suffer from true test anxiety, but the majority of students who claim to have this condition believe it to be true not because of an actual diagnosis, but rather because they get very nervous and may go blank during tests. If I ask a class who amongst them suffers from test anxiety, most hands go up. By the end of the semester, with some coaching, the number is far less. Why? They have learned how to take tests and how to stay calm. If you do suffer from true test anxiety, consult with your counselor right away so he or she can put you in contact with the support services you need to understand your condition and to learn how to conquer it.

Most people dread taking tests and experience some anxiety when taking them. Not surprisingly, the better prepared you are for an exam, the less worried you will be. The best remedy for the stress you associate with taking tests is to be very well prepared. If you know you understand the material, what is left to worry about?

Some people get very anxious before tests because they fear they will not do well. This may be because they know they are not prepared. Again, the remedy is simple: Study well. But anxiety can also arise from a bad past experience. If you have done poorly on tests in the past, your self-confidence may be shot, so you anticipate doing poorly. That may lead to cramming and memorizing instead of truly learning, and may cause you to become excessively nervous during the test, which can cause poor performance. All you need is a couple of good grades on tests to get your confidence back!

If you are a nervous test taker, do not study for about an hour immediately before your exam. Most of my students who complain of test anxiety are frantically reviewing their notes right up to the moment I give them the test. They have been trying to quickly glance back over everything while racing against the clock. No wonder they are stressed when they begin the test! Remember that your brain needs time to process the information. When you cram information into the "closet," who knows what will fall out when you open the door during the test.

If you have studied well in advance and don't get very nervous at exam time, you might want to glance quickly through your notes beforehand, but only if you have time to do so and still allow *at least* a half-hour to relax and mentally prepare for your test. The half-hour off allows your brain to process the information while you relax. Try getting a light snack so you are alert—a heavy meal could make you drowsy during the test. Walk around to release nervous energy. Listen to music that makes you happy. Sit comfortably, close your eyes, and breathe deeply and slowly while you picture yourself in a very relaxing setting— maybe on a tropical beach, curled up on your couch with a good book, or out on a boat fishing. Focus on how relaxed you feel and try to hold that feeling. Now, staying in that mood, concentrate on how well you have studied and keep reminding yourself that:

- I have prepared very well for this test.

- I know this material very well and I answered all questions correctly while studying.

- I can and **will** do well on this test.

- I refuse to get nervous over one silly test, especially because I know I am ready.

- I am ready and relaxed. Let's get it done!

TEST-TAKING TIPS

There are also strategies you can use while taking the test. Let's see what your current strategies are. Complete the survey in **Table 1.6**, then we will discuss specific strategies.

During an exam, be careful—read each question thoroughly before you answer. This is especially true of multiple choice and true/false questions. We know the answer is there, so our eyes tend to get ahead of our brains. We skim the question and jump down to the answers before

TABLE 1.6 Self-evaluation of test-taking skills. For each of the following valuable test-taking skills, mark if you do each one always, sometimes, or never. Highlight any that you do not currently use that you think might help you be more successful.

Test-Taking skill	Always	Sometimes	Never
1. While studying my notes and the book, I think of and answer possible test questions.			
2. I use online practice quizzes when they are available.			
3. I avoid last-minute cramming to avoid confusing myself.			
4. I scan the whole test before starting to see how long it is and what type of questions it contains.			
5. I do the questions I am sure of first.			
6. I budget my time during a test so I can complete it.			
7. I answer questions with the highest point values first.			
8. I read all answer options on multiple choice questions before marking my answer.			
9. I know what key words to look for in a multiple choice question.			
10. I use the process of elimination during multiple choice or matching tests.			
11. I know what key words to look for in essay questions.			
12. I look for key words like *always*, *never*, and *sometimes*.			
13. When I am unsure of an answer, I go with my first answer and fight the urge to change it later.			
14. I try to answer everything even if I am uncertain, instead of leaving some questions blank.			
15. I check my answers before turning in a test.			

even trying to mentally answer the question. Slow down and think before moving to the answers. Otherwise you may grab an answer that sounds familiar but is incorrect. If you have trouble keeping your eyes off the answers, cover them with your hand until you finish reading the question and think of the answer on your own.

If you do not know the answer initially, take a deep breath and think of all you do know about the words in the question. Often this is all you need to recall the answer. This is when those concept maps you made will really come through for you.

Use the process of elimination. If you are not sure which answer is correct, can you eliminate any you know are incorrect? Narrow down your choices. Avoid making a guess unless the process of elimination fails you; however, guessing is usually better than leaving a question unanswered, unless you lose points for wrong answers. On short-answer, fill-in-the-blank questions, and essays, always write something.

After you answer a question, read your answer to be sure it says what you want it to, then leave it alone. Once you move on, avoid the temptation to go back and change your answers, even those of which you were unsure. Often we have a gut instinct to write the correct answer; perhaps we are recalling it at some subconscious level. But the very act of going back is a conscious reminder of uncertainty, and we more often choose something different only because we doubt ourselves.

When answering multiple choice or true/false questions, ignore any advice that suggests you should select one answer consistently over others. Also, don't worry if you choose the same answer several times in a row, thinking the instructor would not structure a test that way. I can't speak for all instructors, but I do not personally know any who give much thought to the pattern the answers will make on the answer sheet, so neither should you.

Here are a few more pointers:

■ Note the wording on questions. Key words to look for that can change an answer are *always, sometimes, never, most, some, all, none, is,* and *is not.*

■ Glance over the exam as soon as you receive it, so you know what to expect, then budget your time accordingly.

■ Look for questions on the backs of pages so you don't miss them.

■ Tackle easy questions first. They may provide hints to the tougher ones.

- Be aware of point values and be sure the questions with the greatest point values are done well. Often essay questions—which usually are worth more points—are at the end, and some students run out of time before reaching them, losing significant points and seriously hurting their grade.

- If you have trouble writing essay answers, recall all you know about the topic, organize in your mind how you would explain it to someone, then write down your thoughts as if you are writing yourself a script on what to say.

- If a question has multiple parts, be sure to answer each part. This is especially true for essays.

- If you are asked for a definition, give a book explanation of what the term or concept means. If you are asked for an example, list an example and explain why it is an example of the concept. If you are asked to explain a concept or term, approach it as if you are trying to teach it to a 6-year-old. Assume the reader has no prior knowledge.

- Be very thorough and specific in your answers. The grader cannot get inside your head to decide if you knew it or not, so your words must very literally convey your meaning.

When a test is returned, record your grade. Be sure to review the test to see which questions you missed and why you missed them, and make notes to go back and review that material. Remember—it may come back to haunt you on a bigger test or on the final exam, and you should know it anyway.

✔ **QUICK CHECK**

How can you slow yourself down when taking a multiple choice or true/false test? _____

_____

Answer: Cover the answers with your hand while you read the question, and don't look at them until you think of the answer.

Through the Looking Glass: **Individual Accountability**

I hope you have gained insight into the learning process and developed new strategies to improve your success, not just in anatomy and physiology, but in all of your classes. One area remains to discuss, though, and that is your responsibility and attitude. When we get frustrated, we often look elsewhere for the cause, even when it may be right on top of our own shoulders. I have watched poorly prepared students transform into honors students and I have seen honors students drop out as they start getting really bad grades. Many factors can contribute to these changes, but a common thread is always attitude and accountability. Here are three facts you need to firmly implant in your mind:

1. *You*, and nobody else, chose to pursue this academic and career path.

2. *You*, and nobody else, are responsible for attaining the success you desire.

3. *You*, and nobody else, earn the grades you get.

You must do everything you can to guarantee your success—nobody will do it for you. That means always accepting responsibility for your own effort. No excuses. To stay on track, you must know exactly what you want and always stay focused on where you are going. At times, you may not feel like you can keep up, but instead of quitting or slacking off, you need to refocus on where you are going and why it matters to you. Always set short-term and long-term goals. Write them down and post them where you will see them often. You are responsible for keeping yourself motivated. Learn to visualize your success—see yourself in your future career. Think about how your life will be. Dream big. Then go after that dream with all you have.

An important part of any journey is to anticipate roadblocks before you hit them. Carefully think of any possible obstacles to your success, then plan around them. You have an unreliable car? Find someone you can ride with in emergencies. You have small children at home? Have daycare lined up and a backup plan for when your child is too ill to go to daycare. You have a learning disability? Immediately contact student support services or your counselor to find out what services are available to assist you. Make a list of anything that might get between you and success, then write down at least two possible solutions so you have a main strategy and a backup plan.

Finally, consider those around you. Family and friends must know your goals and understand how important they are. But do they support you? I have had women whose husbands burned their books because they felt threatened that their wives might no longer need them once a degree was attained. And there are certainly more subtle means of sabotage. Perhaps your friends needle you because you don't go out as much, or they say you're no fun anymore. Your significant other whines that you don't get enough time together. Relatives accuse you of thinking you are better than them because you are getting some education. Realize that when someone changes, whether through education or something else, those who know them may feel excluded, threatened, left behind, even envious. You can try to assure them how much you still value and need them in your life, but don't let them distract you from your mission.

You must surround yourself with supportive people who are happy and proud of you, who celebrate your victories, and who want for you what you want. They will help you succeed. It may be your study group or others around you who will help you study. Perhaps they will watch your children so you get some quiet time. On the other hand, anyone who ridicules you or is upset by your new schedule and goals is really not a friend you want around. Make new friends in class who share your goals and guard yourself from those who would derail you. Stay on track, and you will soon be living your dream. Good luck!

Final Stretch!

Now that you have finished reading this chapter, it is time to stretch your brain a bit and check how much you learned.

RUNNING WORDS

At the end of each chapter, be sure you have learned the language. Here are the terms introduced in this chapter with which you should be familiar. Write them in a notebook and define them in your own words, then go back through the chapter to check your meaning, correcting as needed. Also try to list examples when appropriate.

Visual learner
Auditory learner
Tactile learner
Active learner
Concept map
Active learning
SQR3

WHAT DID YOU LEARN . . .

In the left-hand column below, write your approach before reading this chapter. In the right-hand column, list any changes you plan to make to ensure your success in this class.

What I have done before this chapter

During lectures:

Note taking:

Study habits:

Textbook reading:

My study place:

Time management:

Test taking:

What I will do to improve

List the three areas in which you think your
study skills are the weakest, and ways in
which you plan to improve them.

1.

2.

3.

Here are some additional online resources for you.

- *Cook Counseling Center Study Skills Inventory*

  http://www.ucc.vt.edu/studyskills/aassaform.htm

- *Study Habit Inventory*

  http://www.ucs.umn.edu/lasc/handouts/lascpdf/studyhabit.pdf

- *Test Taking Skills Survey*

  http://www.oakton.edu/resource/iss/testsvy.htm

- *Exam Preparation*

  http://studytips.aac.ohiou.edu/?Function=Exam

- *Concept Mapping*

  http://www.coun.uvic.ca/learn/program/hndouts/map_ho.html

3 Terminology

You Say Humerus, I Say Funny Bone

When you complete this chapter, you should be able to:

■ Break down medical terms to understand their meanings.

■ Build medical terms from basic roots, prefixes, and suffixes.

■ Describe the anatomical position and understand its relevance.

■ Correctly use basic anatomical terms to describe the relative positions of body parts, planes and sections, and general body regions.

Your Starting Point

Answer the following questions to assess your knowledge of anatomical terminology.

1. Most anatomical terms arise from which languages? _____

_____

2. What is the difference between *anatomy* and *physiology*? _____

_____

3. What is meant by the term *cardiomyopathy*? _____

_____

4. What is meant by *the anatomical position*? _____

_____

5. What is meant by the term *medial*? _____

_____

6. What plane passes through the body from front to back? _____

How Do You Say, In Your **Language** . . .?

Have you ever read a computer manual only to find that you are still unsure of how to configure your personal firewall, or for that matter why you should? Has your mind gone numb as an auto mechanic explained all those expensive malfunctioning parts that were replaced to get rid of that mystery noise in your car? Have you tried to read the small print in an advertisement for a new prescription drug? At such times, it may seem as if other people speak a secret language. Indeed,

Answers: 1. Latin and Greek. 2. Anatomy studies the body's structures; physiology studies their functions. 3. Disease of the muscle of the heart. 4. The body position used as a common reference point—standing erect, everything facing forward, including palms. 5. Toward the midline. 6. Sagittal.

most professions have their own sublanguage, as do most academic disciplines. Anatomy and physiology certainly are not exceptions.

Learning the terminology in these two disciplines may be a challenge, but I won't say it is difficult. *Difficult* leaves the option of ducking behind excuses. I have often heard my own students say, "I could do this if the words weren't so hard, but this is just too difficult for me!" Instead, you should think of the words as a challenge, because a challenge sparks the competitor in us—it makes us try harder. Although the words may seem intimidating at first, you will quickly learn tools and tricks to help you understand even the longest terms. Are YOU up for the challenge?

PICTURE THIS

Upon arriving at your long-anticipated vacation destination, you notice how wonderfully new and exotic everything seems—the smells in the air, the people's faces and clothing, the food sold from vendors' carts, and the sounds. You are in paradise! Then you discover that both your luggage and your wallet are missing. You approach an authority and start explaining your situation only to be met with a blank stare. You suddenly realize part of the exotic sounds you have been hearing are a very different spoken language.

1. How will you convey your plight to this person?_____

_____

2. How difficult would it be if you could speak the local language?

_____

3. What could you have done before your trip to avoid this communication gap? _____

_____

Obviously if you plan to spend time in a place where another language is spoken, communication may be a challenge unless you learn the local language in advance. Your anatomy and physiology class will be a place where another language is spoken. Much of the terminology will be new, and most of the words do, in fact, come from languages other than English. You will learn about body parts and their functions by listening to lectures filled with this new language, and you will be expected to discuss your course material and write exam answers using this new language. That is why it is so important that you learn the language of anatomy and physiology. As you study, the first thing you should do is master—not just read, but *master*—the new words. You have to know the language before you can understand and join in the conversation.

Learning the vocabulary is the first step in learning anatomy and physiology. ■

I recommend to my students that they maintain a running vocabulary list. The easiest way to do this is to keep a separate notebook into which you write all new terms as they are introduced (**Figure 3.1**). If you write new terms in your notes during lecture, transfer them to your vocabulary list and be sure to check their spellings later. Once you know that a term is spelled correctly, write the actual definition—exactly what does the word mean? You can find the actual textbook definition in your textbook or in a medical dictionary, but you should also try to explain the term in your own words.

Next, be sure you can use the word properly in a sentence. Try to add some examples that illustrate the term, if appropriate. For example, a tissue is a group of cells organized together that share a common function. Examples of tissue include, bone, blood, cartilage, fat, and muscle. If you are a visual learner, try illustrating your new words if you can. If you are an auditory learner, try reading the words and their meanings out loud and consider tape recording your list. If you are a tactile learner, you might benefit from typing your list into a word-processing file, then alphabetizing it. You might also write the terms and their meanings on flashcards.

You may be surprised at the beginning of the course at the number of new terms you encounter. You can think of the words as a kind of smoke screen—the underlying principles of anatomy and physiology are rather simple, but you may not see that through the smoke. More than one student has jokingly commented to me that "It's all Greek to me." They

My Vocabulary List

Anatomy = The study of body structures.

Physiology = The study of body functions.

Biology = The study of life.

Cytology = The study of cells.

Histology = The study of tissues.

Nucleus = 1. The central region of an atom (in chemistry), where the protons and neutrons are located.

OR

2. The cell organelle that houses the DNA, found only in eukaryotic cells.

Ribosome = The cell organelle at which proteins are constructed (process of translation).

Mitosis = Division of a cell's nucleus.

Cytokinesis = Division of a cell's cytoplasm.

FIGURE 3.1   Keeping a separate running vocabulary list throughout the semester can help you master the language.

don't realize that their joke is not far from the truth—most anatomical terms have either Greek or Latin origins, although many terms are derived from other languages as well. So, instead of thinking that it is hard to learn the science because of all the big words, look at it this way: While learning the science, you will learn some new languages!

✔ **QUICK CHECK**

From which languages do most anatomical terms originate?

_____

Answer: Greek and Latin.

The More the Merrier . . . **Types of Terms**

When studying anatomy and physiology, you will encounter many different types of terms, many of which you will already know. Ideally, all terms used in anatomy and physiology would have the same origin and follow the same rules, but in reality, of course, that is simply not true.

DESCRIPTIVE TERMS

Most terms you will encounter are descriptive, meaning the name is closely related to its meaning. For most students, these words often look the most intimidating—they can be quite long. Yet, once you know some simple rules, **descriptive terms** become quite easy to understand and deciphering their meanings actually becomes fun. Even large words like _electroencephalography_ become manageable with some practice, and just think how empowered you will feel when you can actually converse with a doctor in his or her own language! We will spend most of our time in this chapter working on descriptive terms.

EPONYMS

Another type of term is the **eponym,** which literally means "putting a name upon." Eponyms are terms that include someone's name and have been used traditionally to honor the person who first described a certain structure or condition. This practice led to terms such as the:

- Islets of Langerhans in your pancreas, first described by German pathological anatomist Paul Langerhans;

- Sphincter of Oddi, the "door" where pancreatic juice enters your small intestine, named after Italian anatomist and surgeon Ruggero Oddi; and

■ Eustachian tubes between your ear and your throat, named after Italian anatomist Bartolomeo Eustachi.

Obviously, these terms are not so easily understood. Few people now associate an eponym with the discoverer, making the terms harder to master. Recent practice in anatomy has moved away from eponyms to a preference for descriptive terms, so those will be our focus. You will learn relevant eponyms as you move through your course, but fewer and fewer are in use today.

Of course, there are exceptions. Down syndrome was previously referred to as *mongolism* because the characteristic eye appearance of someone with Down syndrome was a bit like that of people of Asian descent. This term, however, is deemed offensive, so the eponym is now used more often. Another descriptive term for this genetic disorder is trisomy 21, which tells us that three copies of chromosome 21 cause this condition. Although few people know what trisomy 21 means, most people recognize and understand the eponym.

Most of the terms for your course are part of a broader area known as *medical terminology*. Eponyms are still used relatively commonly in medical terminology and in health-related fields, especially for naming diseases or abnormal conditions. You will occasionally encounter them, and you really just need to memorize them as they come up.

TIME TO TRY

Parkinson's disease is also called *paralysis agitans*.

1. Which is the descriptive term? _____

2. Which is the eponym? _____

3. With which term are you more familiar? _____

4. The first vertebra of your spine, located just under your skull, is also called the *atlas*, which is an eponym. Either recall who Atlas was in Greek mythology, or look up his name. How is this eponym also a descriptive term? _____

_____

Although paralysis agitans is the descriptive term, you are likely more familiar with the eponym—Parkinson's disease. You also likely realize that the atlas (bone) holds up your head, similar to the way Atlas from mythology held up the world.

ABBREVIATIONS AND ACRONYMS

Like many disciplines, the worlds of anatomy and physiology are full of shortcuts. After all, some of those descriptive terms grow quite large! You will often encounter modifications of full terms in the form of abbreviations or acronyms. You are already familiar with abbreviations. An **abbreviation** is a shortened form of a word or phrase. For example, the part of your digestive system that includes your stomach and intestines is referred to as the *gastrointestinal tract*, often abbreviated as the GI tract. Valves inside your heart regulate the blood flow between your heart's upper chambers, called atria, and its lower chambers, called ventricles. These valves are known as *atrioventricular valves*, which is often shortened to AV valves.

An **acronym** is technically a word formed from the first or key letters of each word in the full name. It is pronounced as if it is a word. For example, AIDS is the acronym for <u>A</u>cquired <u>I</u>mmune <u>D</u>eficiency <u>S</u>yndrome, and is pronounced like the word "aids." Sometimes regular abbreviations are formed like an acronym by using only certain letters from multiple words. For example, HIV stands for human immunodeficiency virus, the cause of AIDS. But we pronounce the acronym, AIDS, as a word, while spelling out the abbreviation—H-I-V. Many sources lump abbreviations and acronyms together, and surely acronyms are a special type of abbreviation, but now you know the difference.

Abbreviations and acronyms can be problematic, though. SAD is an acronym for a condition called *seasonal affective disorder*. This disorder can be characterized as serious winter blues, apparently brought on by decreased daylight in winter months. The depression that accompanies it can be severe, making the acronym particularly suitable. However, a search of the medical abbreviations section of Medilexicon.com (see Web Resources at the end of the chapter) identified 21 terms that this abbreviation matches, and I found even more matches at other sites. They include:

- Separation Anxiety Disorder,

- Social Anxiety Disorder,

- Small Airway Disease,

- Systemic Autoimmune Diseases, and

- Sporadic Alzheimer's Disease.

As you see, it is important to know the full name as well as the abbreviation, and to consider the context of how an abbreviation is used when determining its meaning. For example, an abbreviation used in medicine is AAA, referred to as a "Triple A," which stands for abdominal aortic aneurysm (**Figure 3.2**), a condition often seen in cadavers in an anatomy lab. This is a weakening and ballooning of the aorta, the body's largest artery, where it ends in the abdomen. If it ruptures, it can kill you quickly. But if I am en route to a meeting of AAA (the American Association of Anatomists) and my tire ruptures, Triple A or AAA—the American Automobile Association—will come and fix it!

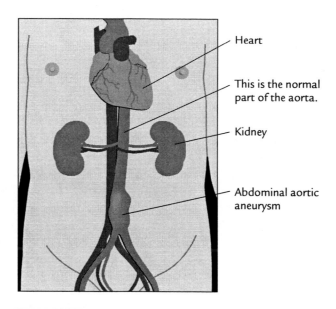

FIGURE 3.2   An abdominal aortic aneurysm (Triple A or AAA).

Here are two last cautions about abbreviations: There may be more than one for the same thing, and some that sound quite similar may be different. For example, a *CAT* scan is an image created through a technology called computer-aided tomography, but these are now more commonly called *CT* scans. An *ECG* and an *EKG* are the same thing. Both abbreviations stand for electrocardiogram, a tracing of your heart's electrical activity—it doesn't matter if you use a "C" or a "K." But, if you change the middle letter to an "E," you are referring to an electroencephalogram, which is a tracing of your brain's electrical activity. Use abbreviations with caution, and don't worry much about them now—like eponyms, you will learn them as you go and it is easier to do so.

When using abbreviations and acronyms, always be sure that you know the full names and their meanings, and that you list the letters in the correct order. ▧

TIME TO TRY

Let's see how many of these abbreviations and acronyms you either know or can figure out. Match the following abbreviations to their full names.

1. _____ CBC

a) Red blood cell

2. _____ ABC

b) Ice, compression, and elevation— how you treat an injury to a joint to minimize the damage

3. _____ RBC

c) Complete blood count—a lab test in which all the types of blood cells in a blood sample are counted

4. _____ ICE

d) Airway, breathing, circulation—the order in which you assess a victim when administering first aid

These abbreviations probably gave you little trouble—you just had to match the letters in the name with the abbreviation. CBC means complete blood count, ABC is the assessment used for administering first aid, RBC is a red blood cell, and ICE is the acronym for ice, compression, and elevation.

✔ **QUICK CHECK**

1. What makes an acronym different from a regular abbreviation?

_____

2. SIDS stands for Sudden Infant Death Syndrome. Is this an abbreviation or an acronym? _____

Answers: 1. Unlike a regular abbreviation, an acronym is a word formed by key letters from the multiple words that it represents. 2. SIDS is an acronym, pronounced as it is spelled.

Putting Down Roots and **Building Descriptive Terms**

Most anatomy and physiology terms are descriptive and are built from two or more of three basic parts:

▇ A **prefix**, at the beginning of the word,

▇ A **root**, which is the main focus of the word, and

▇ A **suffix**, at the end of the word.

New words may be made simply by changing these parts (**Figure 3.3**). Some time ago, when learning English, you learned about prefixes and suffixes and how to use them to change one word to another, and we use them all the time. You will be amazed how many word roots, prefixes, and suffixes you already know.

A prefix is a short addition placed at the front of a word root. Consider the root *cycle*, which means circle or wheel. We can change the specific meaning of this root by adding prefixes as follows:

▇ uni*cycle*—has one wheel

▇ bi*cycle*—has two wheels

■ tri*cycle*—has three wheels

■ motor*cycle*—has a motor

You likely knew the prefixes we just used in our example. When you are reading anatomical terms, don't let the first glance worry you. Simply take a breath and look carefully at the word. Find the root, then examine any prefixes or suffixes that are used with it. Sometimes you may not know a particular word part at first, but you may figure it out by thinking of words you *do* know that include that part. Let's try some.

Plant

Plant-***er***

Trans-plant

Hip ***Im***-plant

FIGURE 3.3   Adding prefixes and suffixes to the root "plant" will change the meaning.

TIME TO TRY

Here are some word parts and examples of words that use them. For each of the following, what do you think the word part means? Look at the examples and see if there is something they all share in common. This technique can help you determine the meaning of words with which you are unfamiliar—first look for the word parts and think of other terms that you do know that contain them.

Word part	Examples	Meaning
Root: cardi-	Cardiology, pericardium, cardiac arrest	_____ _____
Prefix: multi-	Multicellular, multitude, multilingual	_____ _____
Suffix: -ologist	Cardiologist, gynecologist, arthrologist	_____ _____

From this exercise, you probably can see that *cardi-* refers to the heart, *multi-* means many or multiple, and *-ologist* means one who is knowledgeable in or studies whatever the root says. *Cardiology* is the study of the heart, and one who studies the heart is called a *cardiologist.* Note how similar these terms are, yet their meanings are different. The *pericardium* is the sac that surrounds the heart (*peri-* means *around*). And *cardiac arrest* refers to when the heart abruptly stops functioning, such as from a heart attack.

Let's consider the name of your current course: anatomy and physiology. The prefix *ana* means up or apart, and the root *tome* means a cutting. *Anatomy* is a combination of the two. It is the science that focuses on the parts and organization of the body. But, when early folks tried to discover how we are built, all they saw was the outside. To discover how the body is organized, they did dissections—they *cut up* the bodies, *cutting away* outer structures to see deeper structures (**Figure 3.4**). See how descriptive the term really is?

Physiology comes from the root *physio*, which means nature or natural, and the suffix *–ology*, which means *the study of,* or *a branch of*

FIGURE 3.4   Early anatomists explored the body's structures by cutting away the outer structures to see inside.

knowledge. Physiology is the study of the branch of knowledge pertaining to nature. If you think of the natural sciences, which include chemistry and physics, this makes more sense—physiology is the study of how our body parts function, and that is largely determined by the laws of chemistry and physics.

Are you catching on to how easy this really is? Not only do descriptive terms convey a clear meaning, but they are easy to translate once you know the prefixes, suffixes, and roots. You already know several of these, and you will learn plenty more as you go. To help jump start your language acquisition, **Table 3.1** lists several common prefixes and their meanings, **Table 3.2** lists several common roots, and **Table 3.3** lists several common suffixes. Don't worry about learning them all now—they are there to help you start building your language skills. You should read through the terms and see which ones you already recognize.

Mastering word roots, prefixes, and suffixes is the most effective way to expand your A&P vocabulary because they can be recombined into countless new words. ▇

TIME TO TRY

Now you can practice putting your new knowledge to use. Match the following terms with their meanings.

1. _____ arthritis   a) Surgery through the abdominal wall

2. _____ otolaryngologist   b) Surgical removal of the appendix

3. _____ appendectomy   c) Difficult or painful menstruation

4. _____ dysmenorrhea   d) Inflammation of the joints

5. _____ laparotomy   e) Ear and throat doctor

Answers: 1. d, 2. e, 3. b, 4. c, 5. a.

TABLE 3.1   Some common prefixes.

Prefix	Meaning	Prefix	Meaning
a-, an-	without	infra-	below
ab-	away from	inter-	between
ad-	to or toward	intra-	within
alb-	white	iso-	equal
ambi-	both	later/o	side
ana-	up, back again, through-out, against	leuk/o	white
		macr/o	large
ante- or anter/o	before, in front of	mal-	bad
anti-	against	medi-	middle
bi-/bis-	twice, double	mega-	large
brady-	slow	melan/o	black
circum-	around	micro-	small
con-	with	mid-	middle
contra-	against	mono-	one
cyan/o	blue	multi-	many
di-	two, twice, double	neo-	new
dors/o	back	non-	not
dys-	hard, difficult, bad	para-	along side of, beside
ecto-	outside	per-	through, thorough, complete
erythr/o	red		
exo-	outside, outward	peri-	around, near
en-	in	poly-	many
endo-	within	poster/o	after, behind
epi-	on, upon	pre-	in front of, before
erythro-	red	pro-	before, in front of
extra-	outside, beyond, in addition to	pseudo-	false
		quad-	four
eu-	well, good, easy	retro-	backward
hemi-	half	semi-	half
heter/o	other	sub-	under, below
homo-	same	super-, supra-	above
hydro-	water	syn-	with
hyper-	over, above	tachy-	fast
hypo-	below, under	trans-	across
in-	in, into, on	tri-	three

TABLE 3.2   Some common word roots.

Root	Meaning	Root	Meaning
adeno	gland	gram	record
adipo	fat	graph	recording, writing
andr/o	male	gynec/o	female
angi/o	vessel	hem/o, -emia	blood
arter	artery	hepat/o	liver
arthr/o	joint	histo	tissue
aud or aur	hear	hydr/o	water
axilla	armpit	hyster/o, metr/o	uterus
brachi	arm	lapar/o	abdominal wall
bronch/o	lung air passageways	laryng/o	larynx, "voice box"
burs/o	bursa, "bag," (shock absorber between tendons and bones)	lumb/o	lower back
		mamm/o, mast/o	breast
		men/o	menstruation
cardi/o	heart	mening/o	membranes around the brain and spinal cord
caud/o	tail		
carp/o	wrist		
cephal/o	head	my/o, myos/o	muscle
cerebr/o	brain	nas/o	nose
cervic	neck	nephr/o, ren/o	kidney
chondr/o	cartilage	neur/o	nerve
clavi or cleido	clavicle	ocul/o	eye
colon/o	large intestine	oophor/o	ovary
cost/o	rib	op, opth	eye
cox/a	hip	orchid/o, test/o	testes (male gonad)
cubit	elbow	oste/o	bone
cyst/o	bladder, sac	oto	ear
cyt/o	cell	patho	disease
dent/o	teeth	pecto	chest
derm/o	skin	pes, ped, pod	foot
encephal/o	brain	phlebo or ven/o	veins
entero	intestine	plantar	sole of foot
gastr/o	stomach	pneumo/pulmo	lung
genesis	origin	procto	anus/rectum
gingivo	gums	pulmo/o	lung
glosso/linguo	tongue	ren	kidney
glute	buttocks	rhin/o	nose

▶

TABLE 3.2   Some common word roots, continued.

Root	Meaning	Root	Meaning
salping/o, salpinx	uterine tube	tom	cut
scope	examine closely	trache/o	trachea, "windpipe"
stasis	stay the same	ur/o, -uria	urine
stomato	mouth	vas/o	vessel, duct
talo	ankle	veno/phlebo	vein

TABLE 3.3   Some common suffixes.

Suffix	Meaning	Suffix	Meaning
-ac, -al	relating to	-ogen	precursor
-algia, -algesia	pain	-ologist	one who studies/specialize in
-ase	enzyme		
-ate	do	-ology	the study of
-cide	kill	-oma	tumor (usually)
-cise	cut	-osis	full of
-cyte	cell	-ostomy	"mouth-cut"
-ectomy	removal of, cut out	-otomy	to cut into
-emia	condition of the blood	-pathy	disease of, suffering
-form	shaped like	-penia	lack
-genic	produced by	-plasty	surgical re-shaping
-gram	a recorded image	-plegia	paralysis
-graph/y	recording an image	-philia	affection for
-ia, -ic	relating to	-pnea	breathing
-ile, -illa, -illus	little version	-porosis	porous
-in	substance	-rrhage	excessive, abnormal flow
-ism	theory, characteristic of		
-itis	inflammation	-rrhea	discharge or flow
-ity	quality	-scopy, -scopic	to look, observe
-ium	thing	-sis	idea (makes a noun, typically abstract)
-ize	do		
-logy	study of, reasoning about	-stasis	to stop
		-stenosis	abnormal narrowing
-lysis	destruction, rupture	-tomy	cut
-megaly	Large or enlarged	-ule	little version
-oid	resembling, image of	-um	thing (makes a noun)

How to Make a Jack-o'-Lantern: **Combining Word Roots**

When learning anatomical and medical terms, you should know some simple rules. You may have noticed in Table 3.2 that some roots end with "/o." That means the root can be used with or without an "o" added at the end. When the "o" is added, the modified root is referred to as the **combining form**. It is awkward to pronounce a word formed from a root that ends in a consonant letter and another root or suffix that starts with a consonant. For these roots, a vowel is inserted in the middle to make it easier to pronounce. This is most often an "o." For example, inside your body your abdominal cavity and your pelvic cavity are continuous, so they are often referred to as one cavity by combining the two roots: *abdomin* and *pelvic*. The resulting word would be *abdomi**n**pelvic*. Instead, we insert an "o" between the roots to get *abdomin**o**pelvic*, which rolls off the tongue more easily. My students know this rule as the jack-o'-lantern construction.

TIME TO TRY

Combine the following word parts, then define the term.

1. gastr + -scopy = _____
    (stomach) (close examination)
    What does this term mean? _____

    _____

2. rhin + -plasty = _____
    (nose) (surgical reshaping)
    What does this term mean? _____

    _____

3. hem + -rrhage = _____
    (blood) (excessive flow)
    What does this term mean? _____

    _____

▶

4. encephal   +   -itis = _____

   (brain) (inflammation)

   What does this term mean? _____

   _____

5. cardi + myo + pathy = _____

   (heart) (muscle) (disease)

   What does this term mean? _____

   _____

Did you get those? The first two combine to form *gastroscopy*, which means examining the stomach by inserting a viewing instrument (gastroscope) into it. The next pair form *rhinoplasty*, which is surgical reshaping of the nose—a nose job! The third pair combine to form *hemorrhage*, which means excessive blood, and refers to blood loss (bleeding). The fourth pair form *encephalitis*, which is inflammation of the brain. Note that this pair does not require the "o" for combining the two parts because the suffix begins with a vowel. Finally, you combined two roots and a suffix to form *cardiomyopathy*, which is disease of the muscles of the heart. Even though the root ends with a vowel, the "o" is still added—always be on the lookout for exceptions.

Here is another rule to remember: *Spelling counts!* In some cases, changing a single letter can make a big difference in the meaning of the word. For example, two terms that we use to discuss movement of body parts are *abduction* and *adduction*. Note that the only difference between the two is the second letter. However, abduction means to move a body part out to the side, or away from the midline, but adduction means moving towards the midline. Only that one letter distinguishes these two opposite terms. Here is another pair: *ilium* and *ileum*. The ilium is part of your hip bone, but the ileum is the last part of your small intestine.

Realize the importance of spelling—changing even one letter may change which structure you are naming. ▪

Another maneuver that can be tricky with these terms is converting them from the singular form to the plural form. Some of the rules are the same as in English. If you look at one muscle and then another muscle, you are, indeed, examining two muscle̲s, and more than one bone are bone̲s. But there are some unique rules for pluralizing many terms that you will encounter. More than one vertebra are vertebra**e**, and the small bone at the end of each of your fingers is a phalanx, but all of these bones in your fingers together are called phalang**es**. **Table 3.4** shows the rules to guide you with pluralization.

TABLE 3.4   Basic rules for changing words in singular form to plural.

If the word ends in	Do this first	Then add	Examples
-a		Add *-e*	*vertebra* becomes *vertebrae*
-ax	Drop *-ax*	Add *-aces*	*thorax* becomes *thoraces*
-ex or *-ix*	Drop *-ex* or *-ix*	Add *-ices*	*cortex* becomes *cortices*
-ma		Add *-ta*	*dermatoma* becomes *dermatomata*
-is	Drop *-is*	Add *-es*	*anastomosis* becomes *anastomoses*
-nx	Change *-x* to *-g*	Add *-es*	*larynx* becomes *larynges*
-on	Drop *-on*	Add *-ia*	*ganglion* becomes *ganglia*
-us	Drop *-us*	Add *-i*	*nucleus* becomes *nuclei*
-um	Drop *-um*	Add *-a*	*ischium* becomes *ischia*
-y	Drop *-y*	Add *-ies*	*biopsy* becomes *biopsies*

Assume **The Anatomical Position**

Now that you understand how to read and form most of the terms used in anatomy and physiology, we can move on to some areas of specialized terminology that do not fit this pattern. The first of these to introduce is the **anatomical position.** This term refers to a specific body position that is used universally as a common reference point for the positions of body structures.

REALITY CHECK

If you are getting a bit tired of sitting, you might actually try the following positions. If you are feeling a little less active, just envision them.

1. You are lying on your couch or bed, face down.

   What part of you is the top? _____

   What is the bottom? _____

   Which way is left or right? _____

   Where is the front or the back? _____

2. You are stretched out in a recliner—upside down! Your feet are up over your head. Now what part of you is the top and what is the bottom? Next, sit in the chair the correct way. Do any of those positions change? _____

   _____

You likely see from this exercise that our perceptions of up and down, right and left, and front and back may change with changing body position. That is rather inconvenient if we are trying to describe the locations of structures within the body. To avoid such confusion, we always assume that the body is in the anatomical position, whether it is or not. I could just describe this position, but you will understand it better if you try it out, so on your feet please (this one is easy)!

TIME TO TRY

Stand straight and look directly forward. You are almost there already! Be sure the soles of your feet are planted firmly on the ground with your toes pointing forward. Let your arms hang straight down at your sides. In this natural position, your palms are probably facing your thighs. To move into the anatomical position, all you need to do is turn your palms so they are facing forward. Note this position (**Figure 3.5**)—you are now in the anatomical position! Remember it, because that is always the starting point when discussing anatomical relationships.

FIGURE 3.5   The anatomical position.

   All anatomical structures are named based on the anatomical position. ▨

Not only does the anatomical position provide a common reference point, it also provides specific benefits. In this position, it is obvious that the limbs are parallel to the body and everything is straight. You do not see from the outside that there are two bones in the forearm—the *radius* and the *ulna*. When your palms are facing in toward your thighs as you usually hold them, these two bones are actually crossed, but in the anatomical position, they are parallel to each other. In this position, all the muscles, vessels, and nerves in the forearm are also running a straight course.

✔ QUICK CHECK

1. In what position are the hands when the body is in the anatomical position? _____

_____

2. Why is the anatomical position used? _____

_____

naming structures.
Answers: 1. They are facing forward. 2. It provides a common reference point for

Anatomy ABC's: **Basic Anatomical Terminology**

Now that you know the anatomical position, we can introduce some terms that are used when discussing body structures. You will learn these, and plenty more, in class, but students sometimes struggle with these terms. You will have an advantage if you get started on them now.

RELATIVE POSITION TERMS

The following terms are often called relative position terms because they are used to compare the locations of structures. Many of these terms are paired, and that is the best way to learn them. When learning these, be sure to remember to always assume that the body is in the anatomical position.

Superior and **inferior:** *Superior* and *inferior* obviously mean above (toward the top) and below (toward the bottom), respectively. They have all your life, so you already know these terms. For example, your head is superior to your neck, and your thorax (chest) is inferior to your neck.

Cephalic and **caudal:** Look up these roots in Table 3.2 on page 105. *Cephalo-* means _____ and *caudo-* means _____, so these two terms mean toward the head or toward the tail. They are sometimes used in place of superior and inferior, which usually works fine. Just don't use caudal to refer to structures located below the tailbone.

Anterior and **posterior:** I am pretty sure you know these, too. They simply mean toward the front or toward the back. Your sternum is anterior to your lungs, for example, and your spine is posterior to them.

Ventral and **dorsal:** *Ventral* refers to the belly, and you already know dorsal—what is that thing on a shark that you see sticking up out of the water? _____ fin. Yes, that is the dorsal fin, and it is on the shark's back. *Dorsal* means toward the back. For example, your umbilicus (belly button) is ventral, and your spinal cord is dorsal. Most animals get around on all four legs, so for them these terms are synonymous with inferior and superior—that fin is on the top of a swimming shark, for example. But because we walk upright, our bellies are toward our fronts and our backs are, of course, toward our backs. So for us, *ventral* means the same as *anterior* and *dorsal* means the same as *posterior.*

Medial and **lateral:** Medial and lateral refer to positions along a side-to-side axis. Imagine an axis passing directly down through the center of your body all the way from the top of your head to the floor. *Medial* means towards the midline of the body, and *lateral* means to the side, away from the middle. A special term, **median**, refers to being exactly on the midline. Your heart is medial to your lungs, for example, and your arms are lateral to your trunk. Your trachea and esophagus are both in a median position.

Superficial and **deep:** You should already understand these as well. *Superficial* means closer to the surface, and *deep* means closer to the center of the body. In your head, for example, your skin is superficial and your brain is deep.

Proximal and **distal:** These terms are usually the most challenging for students, but they are actually rather simple. *Proximal* means closer to and *distal* means farther away. The question, though, becomes closer to or farther away from *what*? The reference point is some point of origin. This is easy for extremities—the point of reference is where the limb begins—where the limb arises from the trunk. So, in the upper extremity, the elbow is distal to the shoulder, but it is proximal to the wrist. Simply think of where the starting point is—here it is the attachment at the shoulder. Then envision running your finger along the limb, starting where the limb starts. If you are comparing two locations, whichever you touch first is proximal to the other one. Thus, for the upper extremity the beginning is at the shoulder. Tracing out from there, the elbow is distal, or farther away from the starting point. You reach the elbow before you reach the wrist, so the elbow is *proximal* to the wrist—the elbow is closer to the beginning of the limb than the wrist is.

WHY SHOULD I CARE?

During your class, you will examine many structures whose names include relative position terms. When you take lab exams, you will be expected to know these names. For example, you have both a femoral artery and a deep femoral artery in your thigh. If you leave out the word "deep," you are incorrectly referring to an entirely different blood vessel. Similarly, the anterior and posterior tibial arteries supply different areas of the leg, as their names imply.

✔ **QUICK CHECK**

1. Your ankle is in what position compared to your toes? _____
2. Your nose is in what position on your face? _____

Answers: 1. proximal, 2. median.

PLANES AND SECTIONS

We discussed previously that anatomy was originally revealed through dissections, which meant cutting into the body, removing parts, and cutting into the parts as well. Looking at structures from different angles gives us a better understanding of their true natures. But we then need words to help distinguish between these different views.

You can think of a **plane** as resembling a line that passes completely through the body in a particular direction, all the way from top to bottom or from side to side, and a **section** is a cut made along a certain plane. In class, you will discuss body parts that lie on certain planes within the body, and you will examine models and specimens that are cut in certain sections. Let's explore some of them now.

There are three major planes that pass through the body:

■ sagittal,

■ coronal or frontal, and

■ transverse or horizontal.

A **sagittal plane** passes vertically through the body from front to back, as shown in **Figure 3.6a.** You can think of it as dividing the body into right and left parts that may or may not be equal. If the plane passes directly through the midline of the body, it is called a **midsagittal plane** and it produces equal right and left parts. Recall, though, that a term that refers to the exact midline is *median*, so this same plane is also correctly called a **median sagittal plane,** or sometimes simply a **median plane.**

A cut made along this plane could be called a midsagittal section, a median sagittal section, or simply a median section. You will likely see this type of section in lab when you examine anatomical models such as the head or the pelvis that have been cut along this plane.

The second plane is the **coronal plane**, shown in **Figure 3.6b**. This plane also passes vertically through the body, but from side to side, so it gives you front and back parts. In fact, this plane is also known as a **frontal plane.** Your instructor may have a preference for which term you use, but I suggest to my students that they use frontal plane simply because it is easier to remember.

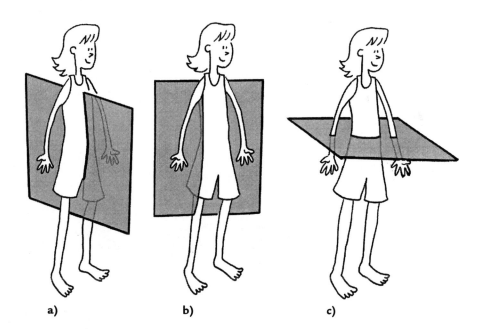

a)   b)   c)

FIGURE 3.6   Major planes through the body include **a)** sagittal, **b)** coronal, and **c)** transverse.

The third and final major plane is the **transverse plane** (**Figure 3.6c**). This is the only **horizontal plane**, and it is also referred to by that name, which is the one I prefer, again because it is easier to remember. This plane divides the body into top and bottom parts.

PICTURE THIS

1. Imagine you are in Las Vegas at a magic show. Suddenly the magician pulls you out of the crowd and places you lengthwise into a large box. (If you can, please lie in that position now.) Much to your horror, he begins to saw you in half at the waist!

   Into what kind of parts are you separating? _____

   _____

   Which plane does this cut represent? Don't forget the anatomical position! Stand upright if it helps you get the answer. _____

   _____

2. Now, please stand in the anatomical position. Imagine there is a zipper running down the midline of your body from front to back, passing between your eyes, straight through your nose, and on down through your chin and neck. Now start pulling down the zipper.

   Into what kind of parts is your body separating? _____

   _____

   Which plane does this represent? _____

3. Again start from the anatomical position. You may have seen circus clowns act like they are running a string in one ear and out the other. Envision that, but change the string to a thin wire and start at the top of the head. Imagine doing that same side-to-side movement all the way down your body.

   Into what kind of parts is your body separating? _____

   _____

   What kind of plane does this represent? _____

In the first part of this exercise, you should see that if the box is stood upright so that you are in the anatomical position, the magician's cut divides you into top and bottom sections and represents the transverse or horizontal plane. The zipper down your midline splits you into right and left parts and represents a sagittal plane—technically midsagittal, because it is on the midline. The final scenario splits you into front and back parts, representing a coronal, or frontal, plane.

Sometimes, though, we are looking not at the whole body, but rather at individual parts that have been cut open. Because they are cut, the particular view is referred to as a section. **Sagittal sections** are common through the head and trunk, but are less obvious in the extremities or in individual organs. For cuts through those, we more often use three different terms:

- longitudinal,

- cross, and

- oblique.

A **longitudinal section** is cut along the <u>long</u> axis (**Figure 3.7a**). A **cross section** is cut directly <u>across</u> the long axis, and is also called a **transverse section** (**Figure 3.7b**). An **oblique section** is a section cut along any other angle (**Figure 3.7c**). I tell my students to associate the "o" in oblique with either the term "off" or "odd" because an oblique angle is off of the main axes, making it the odd angle.

a) Longitudinal section

b) Horizontal or cross section

c) Oblique section

FIGURE 3.7   Sections include **a)** longitudinal, **b)** transverse or cross, and **c)** oblique.

TIME TO TRY

1. Obtain a long object through which you can cut, such as a carrot, a candy bar, or a drinking straw, and some scissors or a knife. (Be careful—sectioning yourself is not part of this exercise!)

2. Hold the object upright and envision the transverse plane. Now lay it down and cut along that plane about midway down the object. What kind of section did you just make? _____

3. Keeping the object in that position, cut one of the halves straight down the midline. What kind of section did you just make? _____

4. Take the remaining half and cut it at any angle different from the first two. What kind of section did you just make? _____

When you cut through the object in a transverse plane, you are making a cross-section. Cutting these halves down the midline makes longitudinal sections. Finally, cutting the object at any other angle produces oblique sections.

✔ **QUICK CHECK**

1. What are three names for a plane passing from front to back and directly through the midline of the body? _____

_____

2. A blood vessel is a tubelike structure. To remove a small section of a vessel, perhaps for a coronary bypass, you need to make two cuts. What kind of sections will you likely use? _____

_____

Answers: 1. Midsagittal, median sagittal, median. 2. Cross sections.

In this chapter, I threw a lot of new terms at you. Most chapters in your textbook will do the same. At times, you may think that learning all the terms is impossible. Just when you think you know the name of a structure, you might learn that it has another name as well. Think about the red blood cell that carries oxygen in your blood. Do you know any other names for a red blood cell? You might—it is also called an **erythrocyte**, or it goes by the abbreviation RBC.

Multiple names are not uncommon in anatomy and physiology. In fact, my students often hear me say "Why name it once if you can name it two or three times and confuse people?" At times, the confusion may seem intentional, but realize that there are many ways to name things—formal names (erythrocyte) and informal names (red blood cell), for example. Mastering the language can be challenging, but you are now armed with important tools to help you. You will also find that many terms are defined in your textbook, either in the chapters or in the glossary. And you can always purchase a medical dictionary or refer to an online version—they are invaluable. If your schedule allows, you might consider also taking a medical terminology course while taking A&P; just don't overload yourself.

But remember the traveler who helped open our chapter. You now know to start your journey through each chapter in your textbook by learning the language. Know the terms so you can understand the material. Don't just memorize words—look up their meanings, look at how they are built, make and use flashcards, and be able to use your new words. Don't get discouraged if you don't master all the terms in this chapter—those tables are long! Get in the habit of talking anatomy and physiology with your study group, friends, and family, for example. Learn what you can now and the rest will come as you go.

People often move to foreign-speaking countries and learn the language as they go. They learn by experience and practice. Students have been surviving in the foreign-sounding world of A&P for ages as well, and you have already had a crash course in the language. Enjoy your adventure!

Final Stretch!

Now that you have finished reading this chapter, it is time to stretch your brain a bit and check how much you learned.

RUNNING WORDS

At the end of each chapter, be sure you have learned the language. Here are the terms introduced in this chapter with which you should be familiar. Write them in a notebook and define them in your own words, then go back through the chapter to check your meaning, correcting as needed. Also try to list examples when appropriate.

Descriptive term	Superficial
Eponym	Deep
Abbreviation	Proximal
Acronym	Distal
Prefix	Plane
Root	Section
Suffix	Sagittal plane
Combining form	Midsagittal plane
Anatomical position	Median sagittal plane
Superior	Median plane
Inferior	Coronal plane
Cephalic	Frontal plane
Caudal	Transverse plane
Anterior	Horizontal plane
Posterior	Sagittal sections
Ventral	Longitudinal section
Dorsal	Cross section
Medial	Transverse section
Lateral	Oblique section
Median	

WHAT DID YOU LEARN?

Try these exercises from memory first, then
go back and check your answers, looking
up any items that you want to review.
Answers to these questions are at the end
of the book.

PART A: USING TABLES 3.1 THROUGH 3.3, MATCH THE FOLLOWING TERMS WITH THEIR DESCRIPTIONS.

1. _____ leukocyte

2. _____ endocarditis

3. _____ subclavian artery

4. _____ antecubital

5. _____ adipocyte

6. _____ mammography

7. _____ mammogram

8. _____ hysterectomy

9. _____ hepatomegaly

10. _____ quadriplegia

a) Paralysis of all four limbs

b) An image of the breast

c) An enlarged liver

d) Surgical removal of the uterus

e) A white blood cell

f) Inflammation of the lining inside the heart

g) A fat cell

h) An imaging technique used to assess the breasts

i) An artery located under the clavicle

j) The area in front of the elbow

PART B: ANSWER THESE QUESTIONS.

1. In what way is the anatomical position different from how you normally stand?

   _____
   _____
   _____

2. Which type of plane divides the body into right and left portions?

   _____

3. Which of the following is an eponym?

   _____

   a) CPR   b) SIDS
   c) cardiac sphincter d) McBurney's point

4. Which of the following is an acronym?

   _____

   a) CPR   b) SIDS
   c) cardiac sphincter d) McBurney's point

5. Which two planes pass vertically through the body?

   _____
   _____

6. Using Tables 3.1 through 3.3, construct a descriptive term for each of the following:

   A condition in which there are (too) many cells in the blood. _____

   A condition in which the liver is inflamed.

   _____

7. Using the tables, define each of the following terms:

   arterial stenosis _____
   _____

   chondrocyte _____
   _____

8. Provide the plural form of the following terms:

   pharynx _____

   mitochondrion (part of a cell)

   _____

   coxa (hip bone) _____

9. What is the difference between *medial* and *median*? _____
   _____
   _____

10. You decide to trim your fingernails into points by cutting at an angle from each side to the center. What kind of section are you making? _____

   _____

WEB RESOURCES

Here are some additional online resources for you.

- *Medline Plus*

  This comprehensive website provides both a medical dictionary and a medical encyclopedia, as well as numerous links to other valuable sites.

  http://medlineplus.gov

- *Medilexicon*

  This site has a wealth of information, including a medical dictionary and extensive listing of medical abbreviations, as well as a medical news section and links to other valuable sites.

  http://www.medilexicon.com/

- *Voycabulary*

  This terrific site lets you open any web page through their program and turns all words in the web page into links to a dictionary. You just enter the web address in Voycabulary, and when the page opens, click on any word and you will get its dictionary definition.

  http://www.voycabulary.com/

- *Who Named It?*

  This is an extensive listing of medical eponyms.

  http://www.whonamedit.com/

- *Word Info*

  This site offers an extensive alphabetized list of word roots, prefixes, and suffixes and provides their meanings and origins.

  http://wordinfo.info/words/index/info/list/A

4 Body Basics

The Hip Bone's Connected to the . . .

When you complete this chapter, you should be able to:

■ Understand the Biological Hierarchy of Organization.

■ Understand the relationship between anatomy and physiology.

■ Understand basic principles of biology that govern body functions.

■ Explain homeostasis and its importance to body functions.

■ Differentiate between tissues, organs, and organ systems.

■ List major organs in each organ system and understand each system's general functions.

Your Starting Point

Answer the following questions to assess your knowledge.

1. The study of tissues is called _____.

2. What is meant by "Form fits function?" _____

   _____

3. Where does your body get the energy it uses for work? _____

   _____

4. According to biological rules, what is the main reason for our existence?

   _____

5. How many categories of tissue are there? _____

6. Which organ system secretes hormones? _____

Climbing the Ladder: **The Biological Hierarchy of Organization**

Now that you are armed with some new language skills, let's peek at what lies ahead in your studies of anatomy and physiology. You have a lot to learn along the way, but your journey is, literally, one of self-discovery—you are learning about yourself. That should make your adventures in A&P quite exciting! This chapter will introduce some basic concepts and principles to guide your path. Let's begin with how your course will be organized.

In science, we like to categorize. One classification system is known as the Biological Hierarchy of Organization. This hierarchy moves from the simplest level of structural organization up to the most complex. Several levels of this system are relevant to the disciplines of anatomy and physiology, and these are shown in **Figure 4.1**. Your textbook and

Answers: 1. Histology. 2. A part's structure reflects the job it does. 3. From food. 4. To survive and reproduce to continue the species. 5. Four. 6. Endocrine.

FIGURE 4.1 The levels of the Biological Hierarchy of Organization that are covered in anatomy and physiology.

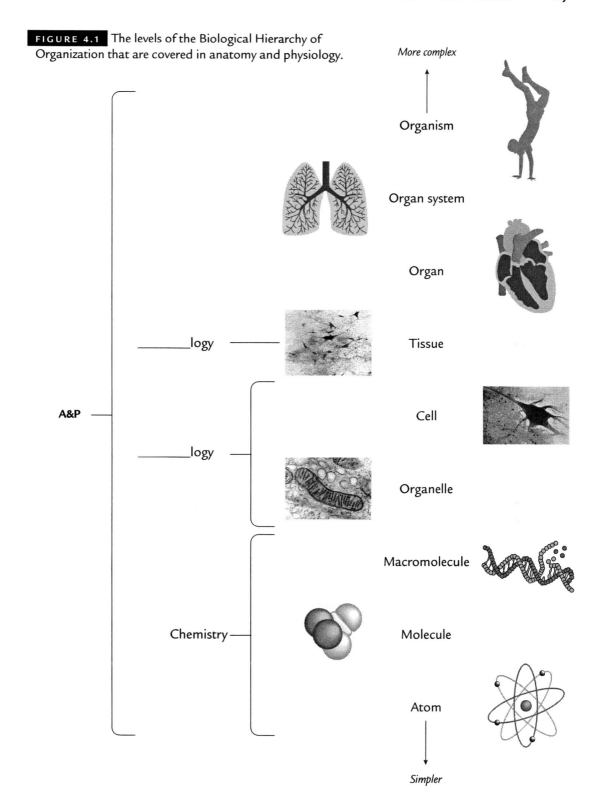

More complex

Organism

Organ system

Organ

A&P

_____logy

Tissue

Cell

_____logy

Organelle

Macromolecule

Chemistry

Molecule

Atom

Simpler

your course will follow this pattern. These levels, from the simplest to the most complex, are the atom, molecule, macromolecule, organelle, cell, tissue, organ, organ system, and organism.

TIME TO TRY

Examine Figure 4.1. Note that the first three levels are part of the science of chemistry. The next two levels—organelle and cell—are covered by another science discipline. Look back at Tables 3.1 and 3.2 and determine the name of this science that studies cells and their structures. What is it? _____

Now, write that name in the appropriate line in Figure 4.1.

The next level is the tissue. Again, refer to Chapter 3 and determine the name of this branch of science.

What is it? _____.

Now add that label to Figure 4.1.

As you see from the illustration, the first three levels are **chemistry,** which we will review in Chapter 5. The next two levels are **cytology,** the study of cells, which we will explore in Chapter 6, and **histology,** the study of tissues. To study both cytology and histology requires magnification, typically through a microscope, so these disciplines are sometimes referred to as **microscopic anatomy.** The more complex levels—organ, organ system, and organism—will comprise the bulk of your anatomy and physiology course. Structures at these levels are visible without magnification, so their study is also called **gross anatomy**—not gross meaning *yucky,* but rather gross meaning *large.*

All matter is made of **chemical elements.** The smallest piece of an element is an **atom,** and atoms can unite to form **molecules.** To understand this, consider water, arguably the body's most important nutrient. One atom of the element oxygen combines with two atoms of hydrogen to form a molecule of water (H_2O). Water molecules are quite small, but some molecules, such as fat, DNA, starch, and proteins, are rather large, so they are referred to as **macromolecules.** Atoms, molecules, and macro-molecules provide the nutrients and building materials our bodies need to stay alive and healthy, and they participate in chemical reactions that do all of the work performed in our bodies.

Macromolecules can unite to form complex structures called **organelles** that carry out functions inside cells. Organelles include cellular structures like the nucleus or a mitochondrion. **Cells** contain the combination of organelles necessary to sustain life, so cells are the first level of organization that we consider to be alive. In fact, cells are the basic units of all living organisms. **Tissues** are groups of cells organized to perform some common function. For example, muscle tissue contracts to provide movement. Tissues then organize into larger functional units called **organs,** such as your lungs, heart, and liver. Each organ performs at least one specific job. Multiple organs combine to form **organ systems,** each with some overall function. For example, the organs in your cardiovascular system are your heart and your blood vessels. The heart is the pump and the vessels are the pipes, so to speak, through which your blood travels to deliver nutrients and oxygen to your cells and to haul away their wastes. Collectively, your organ systems do the work needed to keep you—the **organism**—alive!

PICTURE THIS

You decide to build a house. You use lumber that came from trees, which were once living organisms. Explain how the first five levels of the Biological Hierarchy apply to the tree from which your lumber came. _____

_____

_____

_____

Trees are made of cells containing organelles that allow the tree to grow and form woody material, such as plant fiber, which is a macromolecule. Macromolecules are built from smaller molecules and they, in turn, are built from atoms.

Now let's use the idea of a house as an analogy for *you*, a living organism, to trace the structural progression from simple to complex. Various building materials (cells) are used to form the walls, floors, and ceilings (tissues). You add various systems such as plumbing to move the water in and your waste out, electricity to provide energy, and a heating and cooling system to regulate the air. The latter has a furnace, an air conditioner, and ducts. Each of these items has a unique job, so they are like organs. These "organs" form a complete system (the organ system). Once you get all these different "systems" in place, you have a fully functional house (the organism).

✔ **QUICK CHECK**

Fill in the missing levels from the Biological Hierarchy of Organization.
1. atom, molecule, _____, organelle
2. cell, _____, organ, _____, organism.

Answers: 1. macromolecule; 2. tissue; organ system.

Some Things Never Change: **Basic Biological Rules**

I find most of anatomy and physiology to be beautifully simple and understandable, and I hope you will soon see what I mean. At first you may be tempted to just memorize the names and locations of anatomical structures, but you must move beyond memorization to truly understand the processes involved in the physiology. When studying the course material, always look for the logic and reasoning behind it. Your task will be easier if you understand some basic rules that govern the human body. These rules will help you understand why the body does what it does. There are, of course, exceptions to most rules, but these concepts should still help guide your thinking as you try to understand the "whys" behind your learning.

LIFE BEGINS AT THE CELL

Humans are made of trillions of cells, each of which is, or at least started as, a living unit. Many of our body functions occur within our individual cells. But our cells also have highly specialized functions and they communicate with each other, so many body processes also occur through the coordinated action of groups of cells. In fact, all of our organ systems are interrelated and work together to keep us alive. Always keep in mind that all body processes begin at the level of the cell.

FORM FITS FUNCTION

Recall that anatomy is the study of the body's structure and physiology is the study of the body's functions. Although these sound different, you should realize that they are closely related. You need to understand the parts and how they are put together to know how they work. Similarly, if you know what a body structure does, you can usually predict how it is organized to do its job. A common theme throughout biology is that "Form fits function." This means that all body parts have specific structures that allow them to perform their jobs most efficiently. A part's shape and organization reflect what it does, and similarly the job that is needed affects the structure that a part will have.

Let's consider the heart (**Figure 4.2**). The heart's job is to circulate your blood, and it does this by constantly pumping your blood along its way. To accomplish this, the heart has receiving chambers, the atria, and sending chambers, the ventricles. Some of the blood returning to the

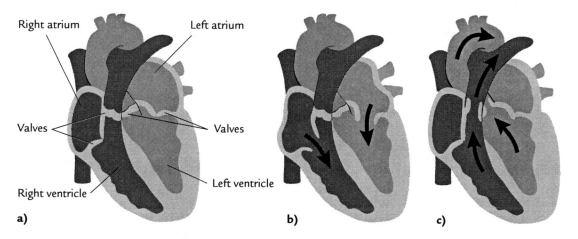

FIGURE 4.2   The anatomy of the heart. **a)** The heart chambers and valves. **b)** As the ventricles fill, valves at the entrances into the ventricles are open but valves at the exits are closed. **c)** As the ventricles empty, valves at their entrances are closed but valves at their exits are open.

heart comes from the lungs carrying a rich supply of oxygen, and is ready to head out through your body to supply all your cells. The rest of the blood returning to your heart has just been to your cells and dropped off much of its oxygen for their use, so it needs to go to the lungs to get more. Your heart is divided into right and left sides. This allows your blood to travel through two different paths—the right side sends the deoxygenated blood out to the lungs, and the left side sends the freshly oxygenated blood out to your body's cells.

Your blood circulates best if it is always moving in a single direction—forward. Doorways called valves are part of the heart's anatomy. One set allows blood to enter your ventricles and the other set allows it to leave these chambers. To fill the ventricles, the doors into the ventricles are open but the exit doors are closed (**Figure 4.2b**). When the ventricles contract, the entrance doors close so the blood must move forward, pushing the exit doors open so it can leave (**Figure 4.2c**). Clearly the heart's anatomy is uniquely suited to its function. In other words, the heart's form fits its function.

TIME TO TRY

Examine **Figure 4.3** to answer the following questions.

1. Figures 4.3 a) and b) show thin and thick skin. Thin skin is found in most areas of our body, but the soles of your feet have much thicker skin. How do you think the thickness of the skin on the soles of your feet is related to the function of your feet?

   _____

2. Let's try the opposite approach. You use your hands to do all kinds of work, some of it physically hard. The palms of your hands experience tremendous wear and tear. What type of skin do you think covers your palms? _____

3. Figures 4.3 c) and d) both show long bones, but the long bones in your hand are much shorter than the long bones of your forearm. How does the function of these two areas explain this structural difference in their long bones?

   _____

4. Figure 4.3 e) shows a top view of a thoracic vertebra from the vertebral (spinal) column. The vertebral foramen, shown here, is found in all vertebra. Why do you think that hole is there?

FIGURE 4.3
Form fits function.
a) Thin skin covers most of the body's exposed areas.
b) Thick skin protects the soles of your feet and the palms of your hands.
c) Long bones in the forearm.
d) Long bones in the hand.
e) A thoracic (upper back) vertebra from the spinal column.

a)

b)

Radius

Ulna

Long bones

d)

Vertebral foramen

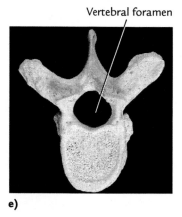
e)

c)

From the previous exercise, you should realize that thick skin is located in areas that get the most use, pressure, and wear and tear. Thicker skin provides better protection for the underlying structures, and because your palms are used so extensively, they are covered by thick skin, like their counterparts in the lower extremity—the soles of your feet. Your forearm contains only two long bones, but there are 19 much shorter "long" bones in your hand. This allows the hand to move into many different shapes and to grip objects tightly, making it one of our most versatile tools. Vertebral foramina are found in all of your vertebrae, stacked atop each other to provide a hollow and protected passageway for your spinal cord and the nerves arising from it.

You already know many of your body's structures and what they do. As you learn the rest, always ask yourself the following questions:

■ How is this structure built?

■ What is its job and how is it performed?

■ How do structure and function fit together?

When you can answer those questions, you are truly learning anatomy and physiology. So when you examine a structure, the way it is built should give you clues about what it does. Similarly, if you know what a structure does, you should be better able to understand how and why it is built the way it is.

✔ QUICK CHECK

What is meant by "Form fits function?" _____

_____

Answer: A part is organized in a manner that makes it most suited to the job it needs to perform. Its structure reflects it function.

 A body part's structure reflects its function. ■

LIFE REQUIRES ENERGY

All living organisms use energy. **Energy** is defined as the ability to do work, so it is required to do all of your body's work, or **metabolism**—virtually everything that is occurring in your body at any given time. Almost all energy on Earth ultimately comes from the Sun and is first harnessed by plants through photosynthesis. During this process, plants take in carbon dioxide and water from the environment and use solar energy to convert these molecules into chemical energy, stored in sugars. Plants also release oxygen as a waste product.

We cannot harness energy from the Sun, so we eat the plants, or the animals that ate them, to get the chemical energy they created and stored (Thank you, plants!). Our cells then use that stored energy to perform our normal body processes. The process by which we convert stored energy into a usable form is called **cellular respiration**, and we get more energy out of our food if we use oxygen in this process. Body parts that are the most active (do the most work) have the highest energy demand, and we must continually supply them with energy in order to do their work.

REALITY CHECK

Based on your current knowledge of your organ systems, which two organ systems do you think help us obtain and use energy from food molecules? _____

_____

Answer: The digestive and respiratory systems.

CONSERVATION

Without energy, we die, so our bodies are very careful about how we use our energy. Our cells conserve energy whenever possible. During the day, when you are awake and active, you use a large amount of energy to meet all your needs. But when you are sleeping, many of your organ systems don't have to work as hard, and you use less energy. If you find yourself in a potentially dangerous situation, your body uses more energy to prepare you to respond, perhaps by fleeing from the threat. But once you are out of harm's way, your energy use again drops. In almost any situation, the body uses the least amount of energy it can to do its tasks.

PICTURE THIS

Our energy comes from the foods we eat. You know that foods have Calories, but did you know that the **Calorie** is actually the basic measuring unit for energy? Think about our energy, or Calories, as being the money of life. To a certain extent, we can control our energy "income."

1. How? _____

2. If we do not take in enough energy "money," we cannot meet all of our energy demands, or, in effect, we cannot pay our bills. What happens in your home if you don't pay your power or your water bill? _____

3. What would happen to your organs if you did not give them enough energy? _____

4. If we earn more real money than we spend, what do we wisely do with the extra? _____

5. What do you think the body does with extra energy "money" it takes in? _____

Most extra energy, again meaning Calories, is stored in the body as fat, regardless of what we eat. This is the body's version of saving for a rainy day, and we gain weight. As with our bank accounts, to lose stored income (weight), we need to spend more than we are taking in. That may be, unfortunately, very easy to do with real money, but your body "bank" doesn't make it so easy to take those extra Calories out of storage because it is designed to conserve energy. It gladly lets you make deposits, but tries to keep you from making withdrawals. In fact, if you cut back dramatically on your caloric intake, your body becomes even more conservative and spends less energy, making it even harder to burn off those extra pounds.

JUST FOR FUN

Check out the nutrition label on your favorite food.

1. First, notice the serving size. Is that the amount you usually consume as a "serving?" _____

2. How many Calories are there in a single serving? _____

   Did you notice that food calories are listed as Calories with an uppercase "C?" This is a bit odd, but there is a difference between a calorie and a Calorie. *Huh?* The Calorie, with a capital C, is a food calorie, which is actually a kilocalorie. So, one food Calorie is really 1000 regular calories. Remember from the metric system that we use the most appropriate unit. For food it is the kilocalorie, but for some reason someone came up with the designation Calorie.

3. Knowing that 1 food Calorie = 1000 calories, how many calories are there in one serving of your favorite food? _____

   YIKES! One cup of skim milk, for example, has 90,000 calories (though I doubt that you picked that as your favorite food)! Don't panic though—those food Calories are the same ones you have always been consuming—all discussion of food uses the Calorie. But how odd it is that just changing the capitalization of the initial letter in the word makes a difference of 1000!

Obtaining all the materials we need to make and maintain our body parts requires considerable energy. To minimize this cost, our bodies recycle. Many molecules are broken down to atoms and then built back into other molecules, over and over again. Think about a child's building block set. Children can spend hours building things, taking them apart, then building new ones—a car is stripped down, then becomes a castle, which is stripped down and rebuilt into a robot. Like the child, the body reuses both energy and materials.

I tell my students that the body is lazy—it prefers not to do anything it does not absolutely have to do. I further explain that, more accurately, the body is highly conservative—it doesn't make or maintain parts it doesn't need, and it spends as little energy as it can.

This theme of efficiency will help you understand many aspects of physiology. For example, the saying "Use it or lose it" is physiologically quite true. Tissues respond to repeated stress by building up and becoming stronger. Aerobic exercise stresses your heart, which responds by becoming stronger and more efficient. Strength training stresses your skeletal muscles, which respond by becoming bigger, stronger, and better at generating force. Weight-bearing exercise stresses the bones, so they thicken to become stronger. This is an important way for women to avoid the devastating consequences of osteoporosis (**Figure 4.4a**). But if you stop exercising and stressing these tissues, all the extra growth and development are quickly lost. Astronauts returning to Earth after being in a weightless state, for example, have lost measurable muscle and bone mass, leaving them slightly weakened upon their return. It takes energy and materials to maintain tissues, and the body's conservative nature prevents it from maintaining any that are not needed.

All living organisms require energy to do work, and the body is amazingly efficient and always tries to conserve energy and materials, avoiding wastefulness. ▨

HOMEOSTASIS

To maintain the utmost efficiency, the body needs an optimal working environment. To achieve this the body has numerous mechanisms, most of which require energy, that work to maintain a relatively constant internal environment. This internal constancy is called **homeostasis**. You can think of it as maintaining the right balance of conditions in your body.

a)

b)

FIGURE 4.4   **a)** Bone that is not stressed during the first two decades of life is more likely to develop serious osteoporosis in later years. **b)** Healthy bone is dense and well developed and better able to resist age-related bone loss.

TIME TO TRY

Turn back to the tables in Chapter 3 to determine the literal meaning of the word *homeostasis*. _____

Homeostasis literally means "to stay the same." Most work done in your body is the result of chemical reactions. These reactions occur most efficiently if there is a relatively constant temperature, the right amount of water, and the right amount of chemicals, for example. We have an acceptable normal range of values for each of these. We know normal body temperature is around 98.6°F. If our body cools too much, chemical reactions will occur more slowly or not at all. If our temperature gets too hot, chemical reactions speed up and some chemicals may be destroyed.

PICTURE THIS

Imagine you have some prized plants growing in your garden. Before leaving for two weeks during a brutal summer drought, you set a timer on your garden hose that will let it run at just the right flow for two hours each day while you are gone. You return home to find that your once-gorgeous flowers are now dried brown sticks! Some investigation reveals that although your water did run for two hours each day, the flow was reduced because some pesky varmint ate a hole in your special hose!

1. Why did your plants die? _____

   _____

2. In the body, water is a critical nutrient that also carries other nutrients and waste products to and from your cells. What would happen to this transport if you had too little water in your body?

   _____

3. How might that affect your cells? _____

   _____

4. How would overwatering affect your plants? _____

   _____

5. How might overwatering affect your cells? _____

   _____

The human body is composed mostly of water. It is the main component of your cells and of your blood. Water balance is absolutely critical in the human body. If you have too little water, nutrients cannot be adequately transported to your cells and wastes can accumulate to toxic levels. Your cells will work less efficiently and may die. In plants, too much water dilutes the nutrients the plant cells need and causes them to swell and perhaps die. In the human body, too much water has the same effect, and when brain cells swell, death can occur. This condition is called water intoxication.

Let's consider another example. Think about how your home's furnace and air conditioner work. You set the desired temperature at, let's say, 70°F. If the air gets colder than that, your furnace turns on and heats the air until it is back to 70°, then the furnace shuts off. If the air temperature exceeds 70°, your air conditioner turns on and cools the air until it reaches 70° again, then it turns off. Notice that there are two possible problems—the temperature can go too low or it can climb too high. Both problems have a solution, but because the problems are opposites, so are the solutions—one raises the temperature but the other lowers it. Both solutions stop once the problem is corrected—they are self-limiting. This kind of control is called **negative feedback**, and it is the most common control mechanism used in physiology and the main way your body maintains homeostasis.

WHY SHOULD I CARE?

Homeostasis and negative feedback are major recurring themes in anatomy and physiology. The normal state of the body provides optimal health. Any significant fluctuation away from the normal range can quickly impair normal function and perhaps become critical. These fluctuations form the basis of disease diagnosis. Negative feedback is the control system by which our bodies correct these errors and restore health, so many of the processes we will discuss in the nervous and endocrine systems will deal directly with homeostatic control through negative feedback.

REALITY CHECK

Let's see what you know about your own body's furnace and air conditioning.

If you are overheated, how does your body respond to try to cool you down? _____

If you are too cold, how does your body respond to try to warm you up? _____

If you are too hot, you sweat more and the blood vessels in your skin dilate to bring the overheated blood to the surface of the skin where heat can be more easily lost. If you are too cold, you sweat less and blood stays away from the surface of the skin to keep your internal organs warmer. You shiver, which involves rapid contraction of your muscles. That activity generates heat.

Balance, or homeostasis, is important in most aspects of physiology. Our bodies strive to stay within normal ranges for blood pressure, pulse, respiratory rate, oxygen and carbon dioxide levels, nutrient and waste levels . . . the list goes on and on. Much of what you will learn in physiology involves the mechanisms by which the body maintains homeostasis. Keep this concept in mind and you will be able to more easily predict how the body might respond in different circumstances and why the body does much of what it does. It's all about balance!

SURVIVAL

We have talked about many themes that govern how your body works, but the ultimate aspect is survival. I often tell my students that the body tries to keep us alive, often in spite of our own stupidity. Think about that—most of us can think of occasions when we did something that was not very healthy. Perhaps we overindulged in something we knew was not good for us. Maybe we tried some insane (and useless) fad diet. Perhaps we went too long without sleep or got dangerously overheated while working outdoors in the summer. Although we *are* our bodies and minds, most of the brain functions below the conscious level to coordinate our bodies' activities, and to a great extent this is what keeps us alive even when we abuse ourselves.

TIME TO TRY

For each of the following situations, think about how your body might respond to try to survive.

1. You are stuck on an island with no food to eat. How will your body get the energy it needs to do work? _____

_____

2. You've been working outside on a hot day and you're sweating heavily. You are dehydrated. How will your body get your water balance back up? _____

_____

3. You have a badly infected finger. How does your body prevent you from dying from a bacterial infection? _____

_____

Our bodies are fairly resilient and rather forgiving. If you have no food, your body will start using the stored calories in your fat and other body materials to provide energy. Of course, it can only do that for so long before you starve, but most people can last for extended periods by drawing energy from their stores. When you are dehydrated, your brain triggers thirst so that you will replenish your water supply, and it also reduces sweating to conserve water. If you have a badly infected finger, your body has defense tactics, mostly conducted by your lymphatic (immune) system, that will fight off the infection.

There are limits, of course, to how much damage the body can withstand but, overall, the body has numerous control mechanisms and backup systems that can undo significant damage, self-inflicted or otherwise. Keep this in mind as you study physiology and you will better understand many of the reasons behind body functions. Homeostasis is maintained to ensure survival. We conserve energy and materials to ensure survival. Our parts perform optimally, making us phenomenally efficient machines with one goal—survival. It underlies almost everything our bodies do.

REPRODUCTION

Did you notice that I ended the last section by saying survival underlies *almost* everything the body does? It is only through reproduction that we pass on our genes and our species survives. Thus even that goal becomes one of survival—survival of more than just you and me. Many biologists maintain that the ultimate goal of our existence is reproduction. Indeed, the vast majority of differences between male and female form and function are tied to reproduction. And this is one area in which the body is not so conservative.

Females release at least one ovum, or egg, each month from the beginning of menstruation until menopause, but few of the ova are actually used. Likewise, each month the uterus builds up materials in preparation for a pregnancy that rarely occurs. Then, the newly formed materials are all flushed away as part of the monthly cycle. The levels of several hormones fluctuate in a complicated ballet each month just in case a pregnancy might happen, even for women who are celibate. Men make and release up to a half billion sperm per ejaculation, and if I know my physiology it only takes one to do the job! Now that does seem wasteful. The sexual act itself is also very energy-demanding.

In general, the more energy and materials the body puts into any job, the more important that work is. For this reason, it is clear why many scientists say that reproduction is our ultimate goal. But please don't feel compelled to rush out and do your biological duty—plenty of folks out there are doing this well enough to cover us! The goal is, after all, survival of the species, so some of us can sit out this dance without endangering the continuation of the human species. But while you are studying anatomy and physiology, keep this biological goal in mind.

 Ultimately, your body functions are focused on your survival, and through reproduction the focus shifts from survival of you, the organism, to survival of the species. ▪

✔ QUICK CHECK

1. What is homeostasis? _____

2. What is the most common way to regulate homeostasis?

_____

3. Biologically speaking, what is the goal of our existence?

_____

Answers: 1. Maintenance of a relatively constant internal environment. 2. Negative feedback. 3. Survival for the purpose of reproduction.

I Have to Learn All This? Does Anyone Have a **Tissue?**

Your course will probably begin with an overview of the characteristics of life, followed by a discussion of at least some of the basic rules we just covered. Then, you will move on to explore each of the levels of the Biological Hierarchy of Organization introduced at the beginning of this chapter. In the remainder of this chapter, we will superficially survey each of these levels. Our plan is to introduce these topics to arm you with some basic knowledge before you go into depth in class. In Chapters 5 and 6 of this book, we will go into a bit more detail on chemistry and cells. Skipping those levels for now takes us to our starting point for the remainder of this chapter: tissues.

Recall that life begins with cells and that groups of cells, in turn, form tissues with specific functions. Tissues must be examined microscopically, and there are four categories:

- epithelial tissue (epithelium),

- connective tissue,

- muscle tissue, and

- nervous tissue.

Epithelial tissues are like wrappings. They form all linings and coverings in the body. Name any part of the body that has a free surface and I will bet you it is covered by epithelium. The outer part of your skin, called the *epidermis*, is epithelial tissue. The outer surface of your heart, also called the *epicardium*, is epithelium. The linings of all of your hollow organs and your blood vessels are epithelia. But these linings often take on a special name—**endothelium**. *Epi-* is a prefix meaning upon, but *endo-* means inside, and since the epithelium that lines a structure is inside the structure, it is called *endo*thelium.

Connective tissue comes in many types (**Figure 4.5**) and one of its overall jobs, obviously, is to connect. One type of connective tissue, called loose connective tissue or areolar tissue, is basically the body's packing peanuts—it fills spaces between structures and is often specialized into a type of connective tissue called adipose, or fat. Dense fibrous connective

a)

b)

c)

d)

e)

f)

FIGURE 4.5 Some types of connective tissue. **a)** Bone; **b)** Blood;
c) Cartilage; **d)** Adipose; **e)** Areolar; **f)** Dense fibrous.

tissue is very strong, and forms the tendons that anchor your muscles to
your bones and the ligaments that anchor your bones to each other. Cartilage is a shock absorber in many joints, where your bones meet. Bone
itself is a connective tissue, as is blood, which is perhaps the body's ultimate connector. There are more types of connective tissue than of any
other type, and this diversity allows for a wide array of functions.

TIME TO TRY

In what ways are bone and blood both connective tissues—what do
they connect? _____

_____

Answer: Bone forms the skeleton upon which the whole body is built, and bones
connect to each other and connect your extremities to your trunk, for example.
Blood travels through the entire body and connects virtually every cell.

Muscle tissue comes in three types. The one with which you are most familiar is **skeletal muscle**. It provides body movement by attaching to two bones. When a muscle contracts, it moves the bones to which it is connected thus moving your body parts or your whole body. This is the only type of muscle you can consciously control, so it is called voluntary. **Smooth muscle** is involuntary and is located in the walls of most of your internal organs and your blood vessels. This muscle moves materials through these structures automatically, without you having the mental burden of trying to remember to do it. But the most specialized muscle is **cardiac muscle**, which is located exclusively in the heart, and is responsible for the contractions that continuously pump blood throughout your body.

Finally, **nervous tissue** is found in your brain, spinal cord, and nerves. This tissue sends signals to your organs and controls their actions. For example, it tells your muscles to contract, causes your glands to release their secretions, and allows you to think.

Can Anyone Here Play **The Organ**?

Now we are moving into areas with which you should be more familiar. Some of the organs you are likely aware of are the heart, lungs, brain, stomach, spleen, kidneys, and bladder. Each of these contains more than one type of tissue. Muscles, for example, are anchored to bones by tendons made of connective tissue and are covered by epithelial tissue.

Consider the heart (**Figure 4.6**). Both the outer covering and the innermost lining, as mentioned earlier, are epithelial tissues that provide protection as well as a smooth surface over which your blood can easily flow. The main bulk of the heart wall is cardiac muscle, which contracts. The heart also contains connective tissue, such as the valves that control the direction of the blood flow. Each of these tissues is needed for the heart to move your blood.

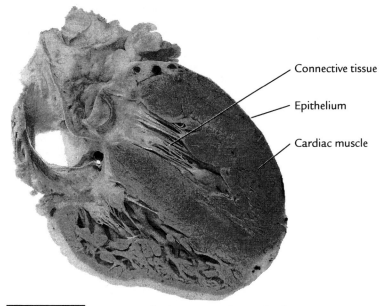

Connective tissue

Epithelium

Cardiac muscle

FIGURE 4.6   An organ, the heart contains multiple tissues.

✔ **QUICK CHECK**

How can the words *muscle* or *bone* stand for both a tissue and an organ? _____

_____

_____

Answer: Muscle tissue refers to any of three types of tissue that can contract and produce movement. A skeletal muscle is an organ, and it is composed mostly of muscle tissue, but it also has connective tissue (the tendon) and epithelium that covers it. Bone is one type of connective tissue, but bones are organs that contain other tissues as well, specifically other connective tissues and epithelium.

In Sickness and in Health: **The Organ Systems**

As you move through your anatomy class, you will do in-depth explorations of the individual organ systems. Our purpose here is to do a quick summary of each of them; (**Figure 4.7**) to give you some background, to get you thinking about how these systems are integrated with each other, and to show ways in which the basic biological rules we previously discussed apply.

THE INTEGUMENTARY SYSTEM

Your **integumentary system** includes your skin, hair, nails, and sweat glands. This system forms your body armor, providing a tough barrier that separates your inside world from the outside. This separation makes it easier to maintain homeostasis. The skin provides protection from potentially damaging substances such as bacteria or harsh chemicals. It helps regulate body temperature. It is also loaded with sensory neurons that gather information about what is going on outside of you, alerting you if there is a potential threat.

THE SKELETAL SYSTEM

Your **skeletal system** is primarily composed of your bones, but it also includes the ligaments that hold them together, as well as cartilage and bone marrow. This system is the scaffold upon and around which your body is built. Your muscles attach to it to produce body movement. It also protects some of your most important organs, such as your brain, heart, and lungs, thus improving your odds of survival. Minerals, such as calcium, are stored in your bones. If the amount of calcium in your blood drops too low, calcium is released from the bones to maintain homeostasis. And your blood cells are made in your bone marrow, so this system is critical to your cardiovascular system.

REALITY CHECK

List any bones you know by name. _____

_____

THE MUSCULAR SYSTEM

Although there are three types of muscle *tissue*, when we talk about the **muscular system** we are usually referring to the skeletal muscles—the *organs*—and the tendons that anchor them to your bones. Your muscular system, obviously, can move your whole body and also parts of it. Your muscles also protect other structures, and they produce heat, such as when you shiver, that helps maintain your body temperature.

Integumentary system

Skeletal system

Muscular system

Nervous system

Endocrine system

Cardiovascular system

FIGURE 4.7   The human organ systems.

Lymphatic system

Respiratory system

Digestive system

Urinary system

**Male reproductive
system**

**Female reproductive
system**

REALITY CHECK

List any muscles that you know by name. _____

_____

THE NERVOUS SYSTEM

Your **nervous system** is composed of your brain, your spinal cord, and the nerves that come off of them. This is one of your body's control systems. It continuously collects data in the form of sensory information about everything going on inside you and around you. It decides if any of that incoming information requires a response and, if so, directs that response, perhaps causing muscles to contract to move you away from potential harm, or maybe causing glands to secrete chemicals that digest your food. The nervous system also controls our special senses of taste, touch, smell, vision, hearing, and balance. This system is involved in almost every body function and has the major role of coordinating all of our organs and organ systems, keeping them functioning properly and working together to keep us alive.

THE ENDOCRINE SYSTEM

Your **endocrine system** includes your pituitary, thyroid, and adrenal glands, your pancreas, and your gonads—ovaries or testes—as well as other organs. This system secretes hormones, which are chemical signals that control many aspects of your physiology. It is involved in normal body growth and development, and in maintaining homeostasis, for example, of water and minerals, glucose, and blood pressure, to name just a few. Hormones coordinate the functions of your various organs and regulate your body's metabolism, which is the rate at which you use energy. They also control your reproductive activities and cycles. Your endocrine system is intimately linked to your nervous system; in fact, the two systems together reign over most body functions and help you survive.

TIME TO TRY

For each of the hormones listed, write anything you know about what they do in your body.

1. insulin _____

_____

2. testosterone _____

_____

3. adrenaline/epinephrine _____

_____

4. A diuretic causes the body to lose water, usually by increasing urination. What do you think the hormone called *antidiuretic hormone* does? _____

_____

Answers: 1. Insulin regulates blood glucose (sugar) by decreasing it, moving glucose into the cells to be stored for later use. 2. Testosterone is a sex hormone found in highest concentrations in males, causing many sex characteristics associated with maleness, and also contributing to the sex drive in both genders. 3. Adrenaline or epinephrine gives you that adrenaline rush—increased pulse, respiration, blood pressure, and makes you keenly alert and prepared for action in times of crisis. 4. Antidiuretic hormone causes the body to retain water—it has the opposite effect of a diuretic.

THE CARDIOVASCULAR SYSTEM

As mentioned earlier, the **cardiovascular system** includes your heart, blood vessels, and the blood within them. This system circulates your blood, which carries nutrients, hormones, water, oxygen, and wastes, delivering the good stuff to the cells and carrying the bad stuff elsewhere in the body so it can be recycled or discarded. These functions are essential for homeostasis, growth and development, and reproduction. This system also helps regulate your body temperature and provides a common link between all cells. And we all know what happens to the organism if the heart quits.

REALITY CHECK

List any blood vessels you know by name. _____

_____

THE LYMPHATIC SYSTEM

Your **lymphatic system** contains your spleen, thymus, tonsils, lymphatic vessels, and lymph nodes. This system has two major jobs. It is an alternative return route that picks up extra fluid and materials from your tissues and returns them to your blood, helping to maintain your blood volume and blood pressure. But the function of which you are most likely aware is your lymphatic system's role in keeping you healthy. This system is also referred to as your *immune system*, and it helps fight infection and disease.

THE RESPIRATORY SYSTEM

Your **respiratory system** includes your nose, larynx (voice box), trachea (windpipe), bronchi, and lungs. This system is designed to bring air into and out of the lungs so that the blood can drop off the carbon dioxide it picked up from the cells and pick up a fresh supply of oxygen. Blood from your lungs returns to your heart and shoots out through your body so that the oxygen it just gained can be used by your cells to harness energy from your food, allowing your cells to do their work. This cellular process generates carbon dioxide that is picked up by the blood and carried back to the heart to be routed back to the lungs to exchange gases once again—carbon dioxide out, oxygen in. From this, you can see that your respiratory system is directly tied to your cell's energy use. In addition, air that passes across your vocal cords causes them to vibrate, producing sound—perhaps so you can sing love songs to your sweetie with that goal of reproduction in mind!

THE DIGESTIVE SYSTEM

Your **digestive system** includes your mouth, salivary glands, pharynx (throat), esophagus, stomach, pancreas, liver, small intestine, and large intestine. This system brings food into your body and breaks it down to small molecules that enter your blood. These molecules then provide nutrients, building materials for growth and repair, and the chemical energy that your cells use to do your body's work. The digestive system also allows the body to get rid of wastes from the liver, as well as whatever you eat that is not absorbed into your body.

THE URINARY SYSTEM

The **urinary system** includes two kidneys, two ureters, the urinary bladder, and the urethra. This system filters your blood, getting rid of waste products and keeping what the body needs, thus maintaining homeostasis. It is crucial for maintaining the proper balance of water, minerals, glucose, blood volume and pressure, and pH in your body. Its role in ridding the body of wastes led to its alternative name—the excretory system.

✔ **QUICK CHECK**

The respiratory, digestive, and urinary systems all allow the body to get rid of wastes. How do all three systems do this? _____

_____

_____

Answer: The respiratory system gets rid of the waste gas, carbon dioxide, when you exhale. Through defecation, the digestive system gets rid of wastes from the liver and the leftovers from eating that our bodies don't absorb. The urinary system cleanses our blood of wastes and excess materials through urination.

THE REPRODUCTIVE SYSTEM

Finally, your **reproductive system** has different organs depending on your gender. Males have testes, epididymes, the vasa deferentia, seminal vesicles, prostate gland, penis, and scrotum. The male reproductive system produces sperm to fertilize the female's ovum, making Dad's contribution to the baby's genetic makeup.

The female reproductive system includes the ovaries, uterine tubes (oviducts), uterus, vagina, clitoris, labia, and mammary glands. A woman's system is designed to produce the ova that can be fertilized to create a new life, with Mom contributing the other half of the baby's genetic makeup. If pregnancy occurs, her uterus becomes the baby's home during its initial nine months of development, and her mammary glands can feed the baby after it is born.

Together, all of your organ systems carry out all the functions needed to keep you—the organism—alive and, usually, healthy. These systems are all coordinated and interrelated, and illness or malfunction in one often leads to imbalance and malfunction in another. The human organism is, at once, a marvel of complexity and a showcase of simplicity, unsurpassed in its precision by any man-made machine. Take great pride in who you are, for you are a chemical and mechanical miracle!

Final Stretch!

Now that you have finished reading this chapter, it is time to stretch your brain a bit and check how much you learned.

RUNNING WORDS

At the end of each chapter, be sure you have learned the language. Here are the terms introduced in this chapter with which you should be familiar. Write them in a notebook and define them in your own words, then go back through the chapter to check your meaning, correcting as needed. Also try to list examples when appropriate.

Chemistry	Organelle	Smooth muscle
Cytology	Cell	Cardiac muscle
Histology	Tissue	Nervous tissue
Microscopic anatomy	Organ	Integumentary
Gross anatomy	Organ system	system
Chemical element	Organism	Skeletal system
Atom	Energy	Muscular system
Molecule	Metabolism	Nervous system
Macromolecule	Cellular respiration	Endocrine system
	Calorie	Cardiovascular
	Conservation	system
	Homeostasis	Lymphatic system
	Negative feedback	Respiratory system
	Epithelial tissue	Digestive system
	Endothelium	Urinary system
	Connective tissue	Reproductive system
	Muscle tissue	
	Skeletal muscle	

WHAT DID YOU LEARN?

Try these exercises from memory first, then go back and check your answers, looking up any items that you want to review. Answers to these questions are at the end of the book.

PART A: ANSWER THE FOLLOWING QUESTIONS.

1. List, in order from most complex to simplest, the levels of the Biological Hierarchy of Organization that are relevant to anatomy and physiology. _____

_____

_____

2. Examine your foot. It transmits your body weight to the ground and supports you in an upright position. How does your foot demonstrate that form fits function?

_____

_____

3. Where do we get the energy we use for body processes? _____

4. How is energy related to your body weight?

_____

_____

5. What is homeostasis and why is it important? _____

_____

_____

_____

6. What are the four general types of tissues?

_____

_____

PART B: MATCH THE TERMS ON THE LEFT WITH ALL OF THEIR DESCRIPTIONS ON THE RIGHT.

1. _____ muscle

2. _____ lymphatic

3. _____ epithelium

4. _____ organelle

5. _____ bone

6. _____ heart

7. _____ cardiovascular

8. _____ nervous

a) A functional part of a cell

b) An organ

c) A tissue

d) An organ system

e) Covers or lines body parts

f) Skeletal system

g) Controls most body functions

h) Keeps you healthy

WEB RESOURCES

Here are some additional online resources for you.

- *Innerbody.com*

  This interactive website offers animations, tutorials, and descriptions of items from anatomy. You can click on any organ system for an interactive diagram, then click on most structures to get more information.

  http://www.innerbody.com

- *Health Information*

  This website from the National Institutes of Health is loaded with information and includes a section on Body Systems.

  http://health.nih.gov

- *Atlas of Histology*

  This website from the University of Illinois College of Medicine provides a wide array of online histology slides.

  http://www.med.uiuc.edu/histo

CHAPTER 1

Answers will vary from student to student.

CHAPTER 2

Part A
1. −32
2. 20,000
3. 3/4
4. 1/4
5. 1/4
6. 0.2
7. 720 breaths per hour
8. 400 cm
9. 51 kg

Part B
1. 14
2. 4
3. 0.3; 30%
4. 20%
5. volume of a liquid
6. gram; meter (technically kilometer, but in practical use it is the meter); liter
7. "Normal" blood pressure is the average blood pressure.
8. 100°C
9. volume
10. 1000

CHAPTER 3

Part A
1. e
2. f
3. i
4. j
5. g
6. h
7. b
8. d
9. c
10. a

Part B
1. In the anatomical position, your palms are facing forward.
2. sagittal
3. d
4. b
5. coronal and sagittal
6. polycythemia; hepatitis
7. abnormal narrowing of the arteries; cartilage cell
8. pharynges; mitochondria; coxae
9. *Medial* is a comparative term meaning a designated object is closer to the midline; *median* means a structure is positioned exactly on the midline.
10. oblique

CHAPTER 4

Part A

1. organism, organ system, organ, tissue, cell, organelle, macromolecule, molecule, atom

2. The foot is a broadened surface with arches that distribute the weight evenly to all parts of the foot that contact the ground.

3. from the food we eat

4. If you consume too much energy (Calories), you gain weight; if you spend more energy than you consume, you lose weight; and if your caloric expenditure equals your caloric intake, your weight remains constant.

5. Homeostasis is the maintenance of a constant internal environment. It is important to maintain homeostasis because cells perform optimally in a balanced internal environment.

6. epithelial, connective, nervous, muscle

Part B

1. b, c
2. d, h
3. c, e
4. a
5. b, c, f
6. b
7. d
8. c, d, g

Photo and Illustration Credits

Unless noted, all chapter opener art and cartoon spot art was created by Kevin Opstedal.

CHAPTER 1

Table 1.2: All photos from PhotoDisc.

Figures 1.1, 1.2, 1.3, 1.4: Seventeenth Street Studios.

Figure 1.5: Tom Stewart/CORBIS.

CHAPTER 2

Figures 2.1, 2.2, 2.3, 2.4, 2.5: Seventeenth Street Studios.

Figure 2.6: Benjamin Cummings Publishing, Pearson Education.

Figure 2.7a: Ohaus Corporation.

Figure 2.7b: Seventeenth Street Studios.

Figure 2.8: Richard Megna/ Fundamental Photographs.

Figures 2.9, 2.10, 2.11: Seventeenth Street Studios.

CHAPTER 3

Figures 3.1, 3.2: Seventeenth Street Studios.

Figure 3.3; hip implant: National Institutes of Health. Art by Seventeenth Street Studios.

Figure 3.4: Victoria & Albert Museum, London/Art Resource, NY.

Figures 3.5, 3.6: Kevin Opstedal.

Figure 3.7: Seventeenth Street Studios.

CHAPTER 4

Figure 4.1; tissue: Benjamin Cummings Publishing, Pearson Education.

Figure 4.1; cell: Ed Reschke/Peter Arnold.

Figure 4.1; organelle: Don W. Fawcett/Visuals Unlimited.

Figure 4.1; art: Seventeenth Street Studios.

Figure 4.2: Seventeenth Street Studios.

Figure 4.3a, b: Frederick Skvara/Visuals Unlimited.

Figure 4.3c, d, e: Ralph T. Hutchings.

Figure 4.4a: P. Motta/Photo Researchers.

Figure 4.4b: Steve Gschmeissner/SPL/Photo Researchers.

Figure 4.5a, b, c: Benjamin Cummings Publishing, Pearson Education.

Figure 4.5d: Carolina Biological/Visuals Unlimited.

Figures 4.5e, f: Benjamin Cummings Publishing, Pearson Education.

Figure 4.6: David L. Bassett

Figure 4.7: Adapted from Marieb, *Essentials of Human Anatomy & Physiology*, 8e, F1.2, © Benjamin Cummings, 2006.

CHAPTER 5

Figure 5.1; tissue: Benjamin Cummings Publishing, Pearson Education.

Figure 5.1; cell: Ed Reschke/Peter Arnold.

Figure 5.1; organelle: Don W. Fawcett/Visuals Unlimited.

Figure 5.1, art: Seventeenth Street Studios.

Figures 5.2, 5.3, 5.4, Time to Try, p. 172, 5.5, 5.6, 5.7, 5.8, 5.9, 5.10: Seventeenth Street Studios.

Figure 5.8, photo: Lori Garrett.

CHAPTER 6

Figure 6.1; tissue: Benjamin Cummings Publishing, Pearson Education.

Figure 6.1; cell: Ed Reschke/Peter Arnold.

Figure 6.1; organelle: Don W. Fawcett/Visuals Unlimited.

Figure 6.1, art: Seventeenth Street Studios.

Figure 6.2a: Dennis Kunkel/Visuals Unlimited.

Figure 6.2b: David McCarthy/Photo Researchers.

Figure 6.2c: David M. Phillips/Photo Researchers.

Figure 6.4: Seventeenth Street Studios.

Figure 6.5: Adapted from Marieb, *Study Guide* for *Human Anatomy & Physiology*, 6e, F3.1, © Benjamin Cummings, 2004.

Figure 6.6: Seventeenth Street Studios.

Figure 6.7: D.W. Fawcett/Photo Researchers/Adapted from Bauman, *Microbiology*, F3.37, © Benjamin Cummings, 2004.

Figures 6.8, 6.9, 6.10: Seventeenth Street Studios.

Figure 6.11a, b, c: M. Sheetz, R. Painter, and S. Singer, *Journal of Cell Biology* 1976. 70: 193.

Figure 6.12: Birgit H. Satir, Dept. of Anatomy and Structural Biology, Albert Einstein College of Medicine.

Figure 6.13: Seventeenth Street Studios.

Table 6.2: All photos by Ed Reschke.